20th edition

The Art Book

2008

www.theartbook.com

Cover Illustrations
David Hitch/Arena

Design
Magnet Harlequin Ltd
T +44 (0) 1895 432400
F +44 (0) 1895 432440
E sales@magharl.co.uk

Digital Colour Management
Magnet Harlequin Ltd
T +44 (0) 1895 432400
F +44 (0) 1895 432440
E sales@magharl.co.uk

Printing and Binding
Everbest Printing Co Ltd, China
All UK and European enquiries
T + 44 (0) 20 8876 8666
T + 44 (0) 20 8487 5819
E art@theartbook.com

Publisher
The John Pidgeon Consultancy Ltd.
Claridge House, 29 Barnes High Street,
London SW13 9LW, England
T + 44 (0) 20 8876 8666
T + 44 (0) 20 8487 5819
E art@theartbook.com
W www.theartbook.com

ISBN 1 899034 65 X

Contents

The Art Book 2008

Cover Competition

It is now 20 years since the first edition of The Art Book was published and many of the most talented, innovative and progressive agencies in the UK have been involved in The Art Book for most if not all of those 20 years.

David Hitch
Arena

This year therefore we looked to these same talented people to be the judges of the competition to find the best cover for The Art Book 2008 and were delighted with the winning entry from David Hitch of Arena.

The following artists were talented runners up.

David Hitch
Arena

Simon Stephenson
Nb illustration

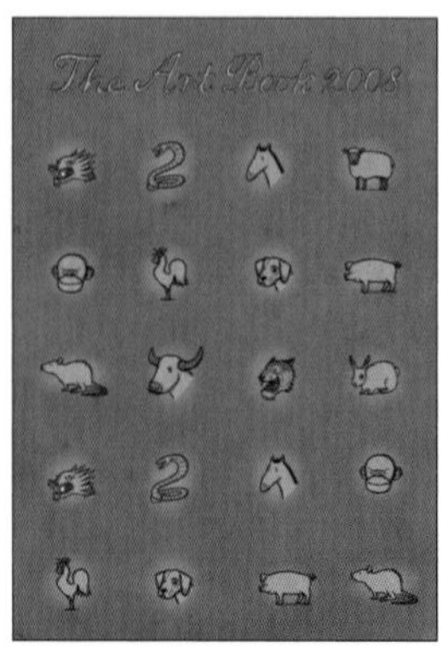

Frances Castle
Arena

Julian De Narvaez
Folio

a
advocate art
mail@advocate-art.com
39 church road wimbledon village
london sw19 5dq +44 (0) 20 8879 1166
illustrate your point
Alma Larroca
Annick Poirier
Arnauld Tracol
Arron Lindsay
Aurore Colson
Benjamin Savignac
Chellie Caroll
Dan Alexander
Dwayne Bell
Ed Taylor
Eelco van den Berg
Finn Neary
Gabriel Moreno
Graeme Bandeira
Guy Boucault
Jen Geduzzi
Joanne Nelson
Jonathan Schofield
Liz Clements
Michael Worthy
Murilo Maciel
Neil Duerden
Owen Phillips
Owen Rimmington
Paco Krijnen
Pablo Pasadas
Peter Mac
Peter Greenwood
Pierre-Paul Pariseau
Rubens Lp
Rebecca Terborg
Sarah Horne
Sergey Shinjaev
Thomas Moon
Tom Lane
Vicky Newman
Illustration: Neil Duerden
Photography : James Lightbown
Fashion : Vivienne Westwood

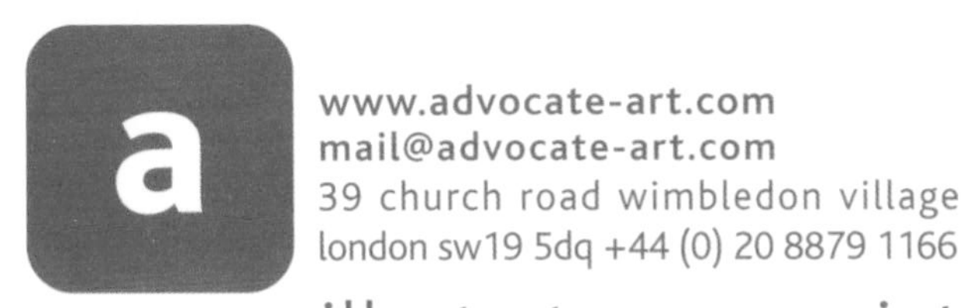

arron lindsay | advocate-art.com

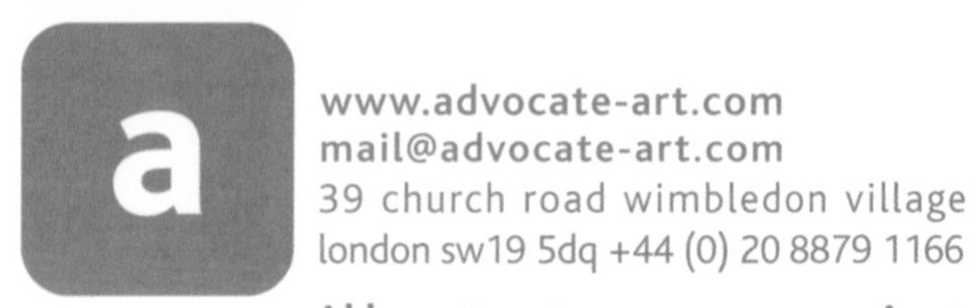

advocate art illustrate your point

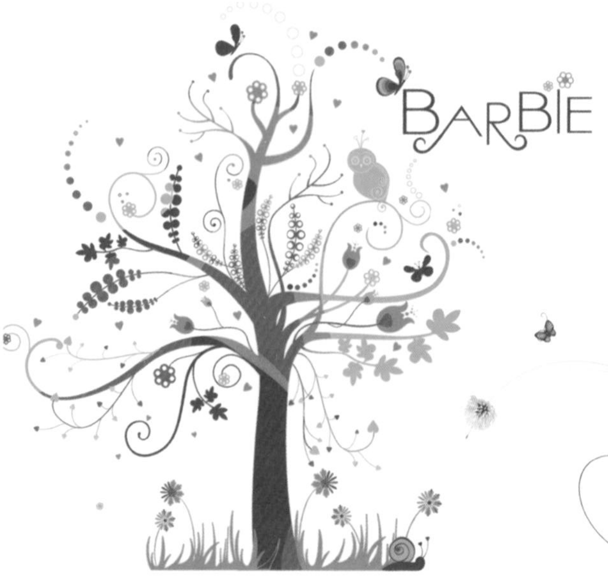

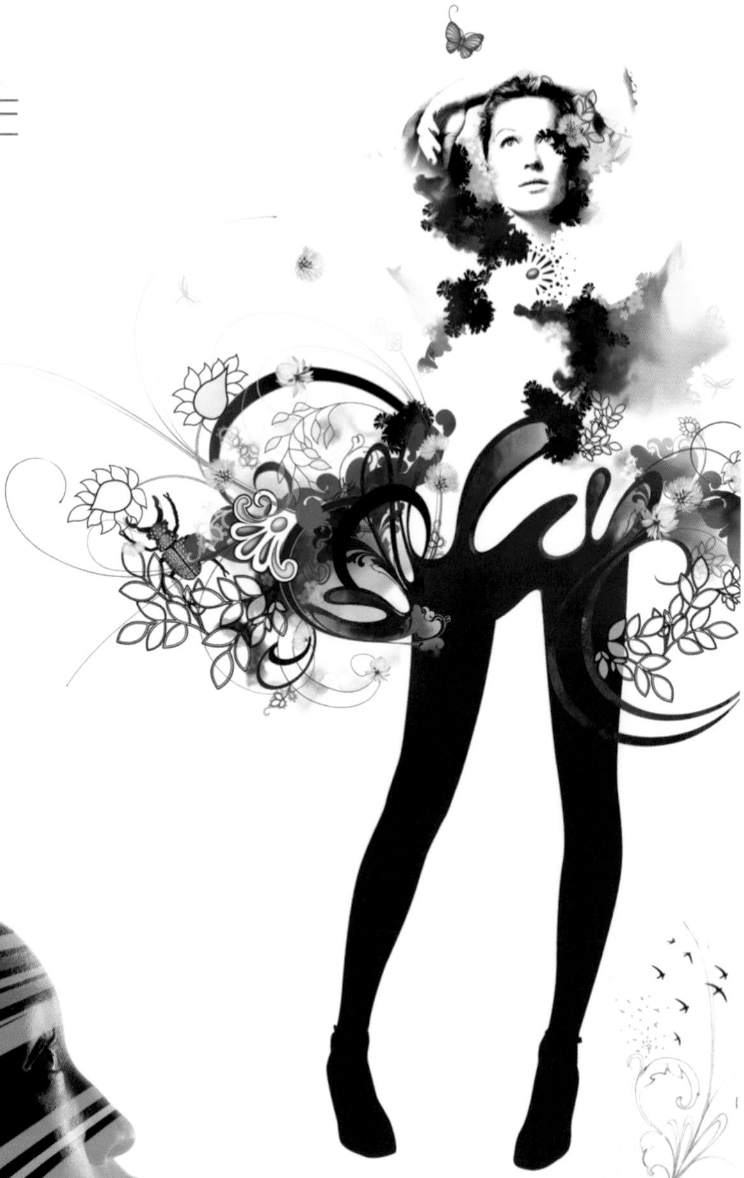

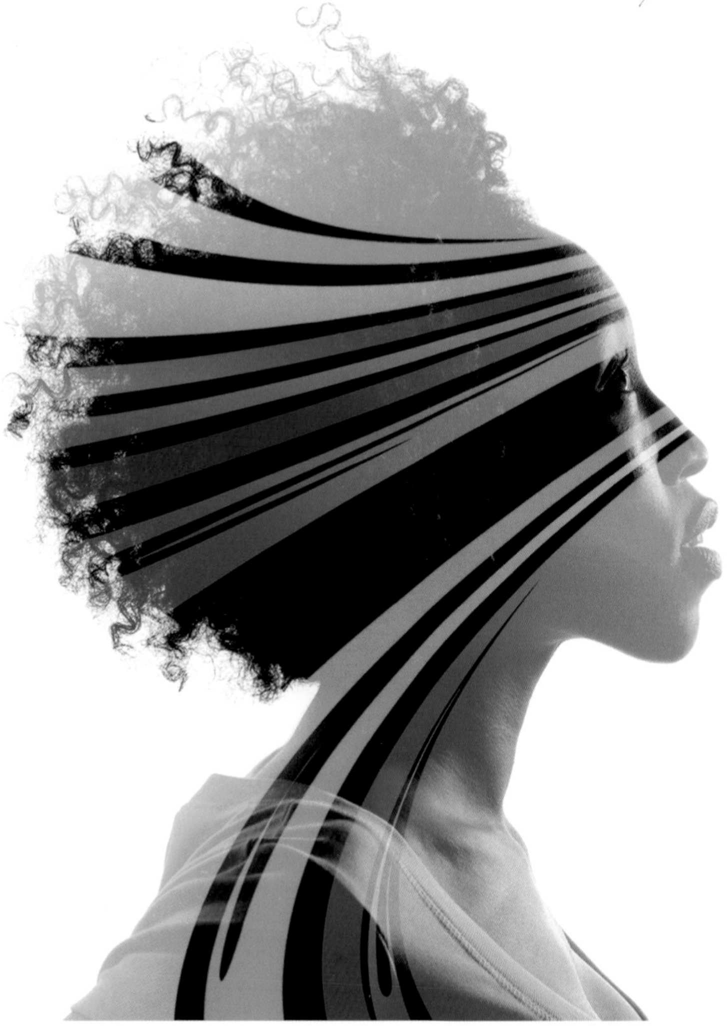

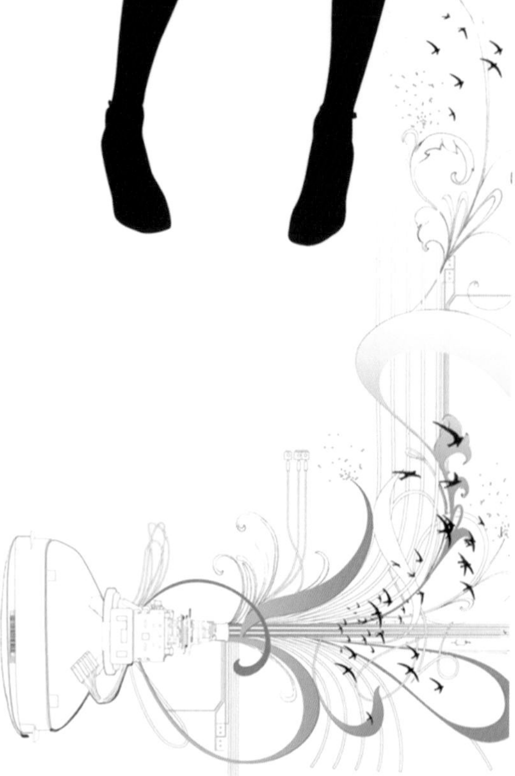

chellie carroll | advocate-art.com

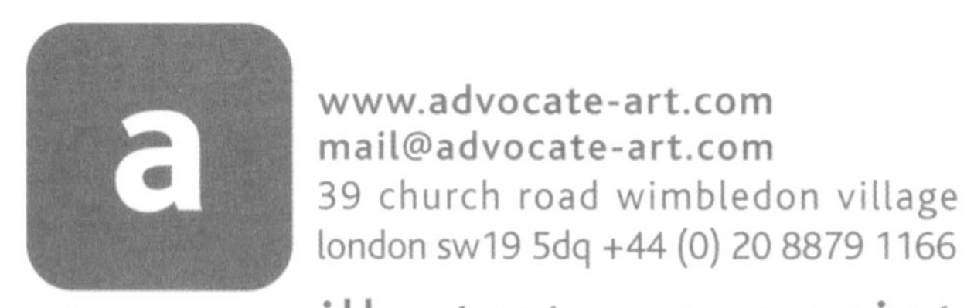

michael worthy | advocate-art.com

www.advocate-art.com
mail@advocate-art.com
39 church road wimbledon village
london sw19 5dq +44 (0) 20 8879 1166
advocate art illustrate your point

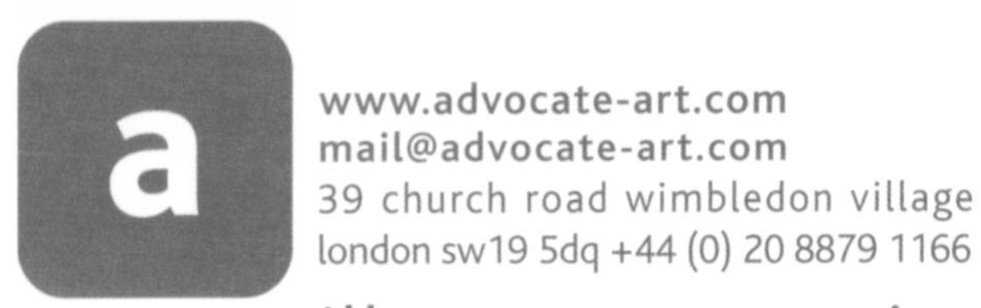

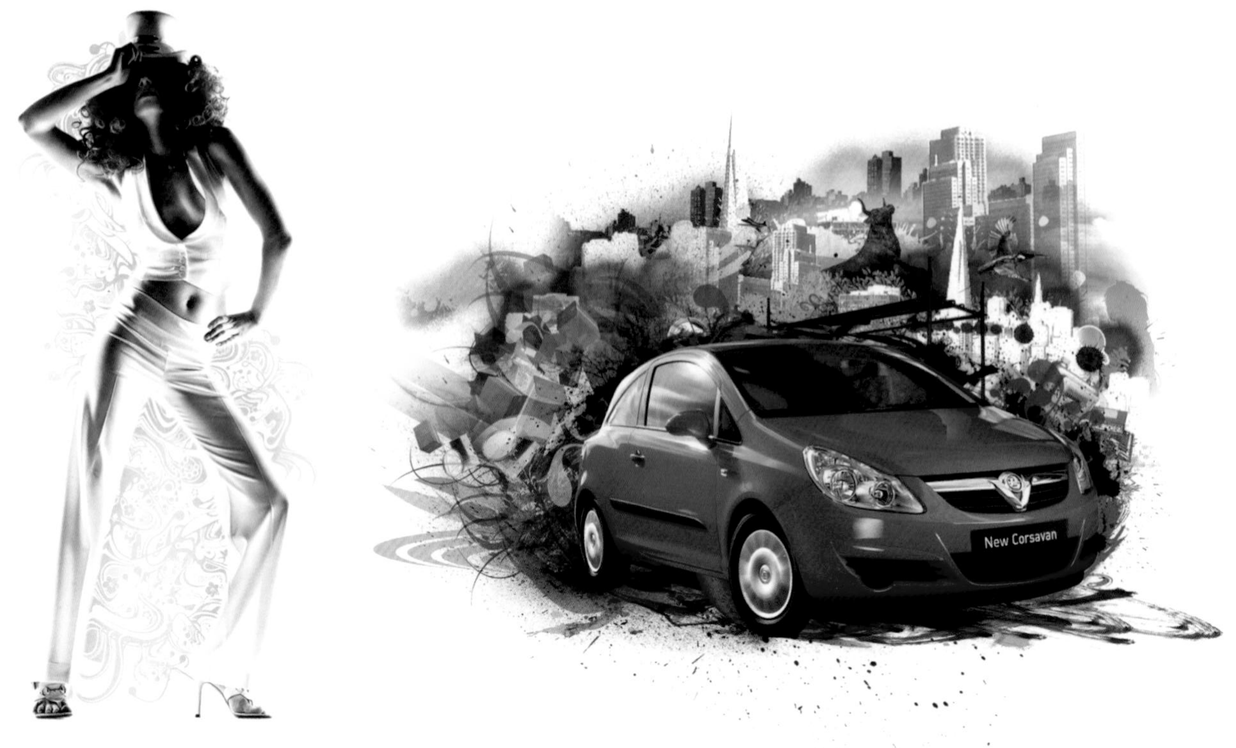

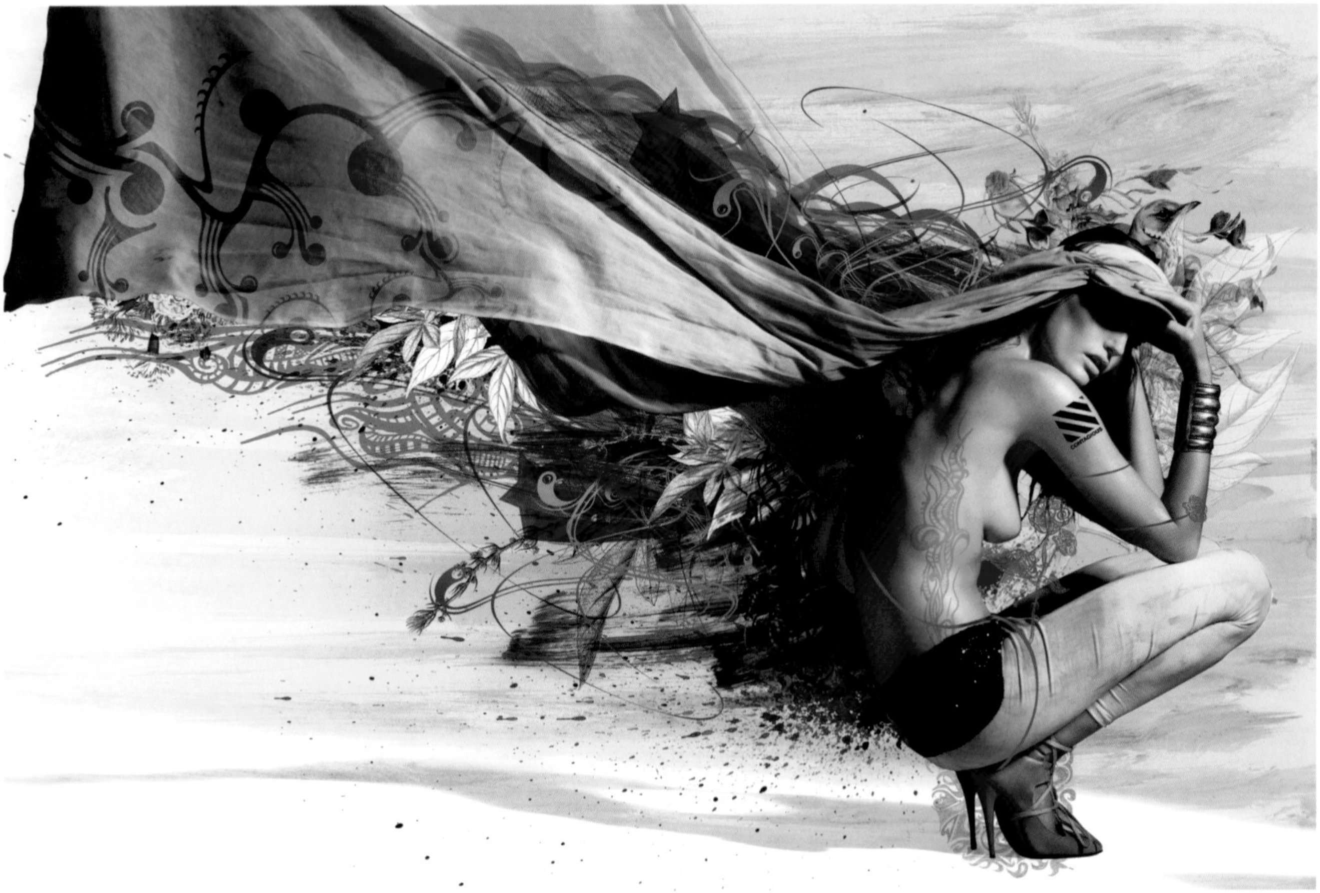

neil duerden | advocate-art.com

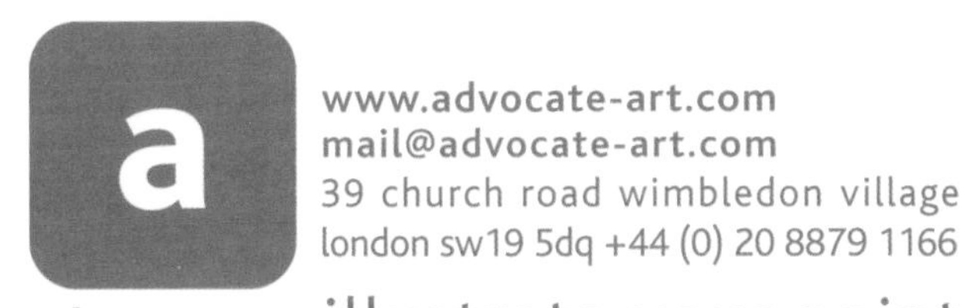

owen phillips | advocate-art.com

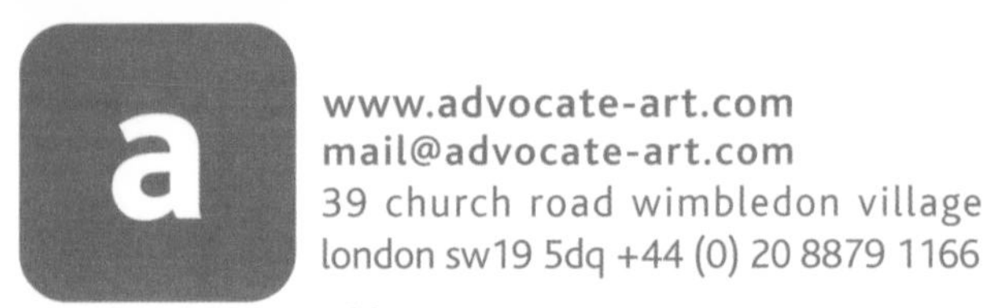

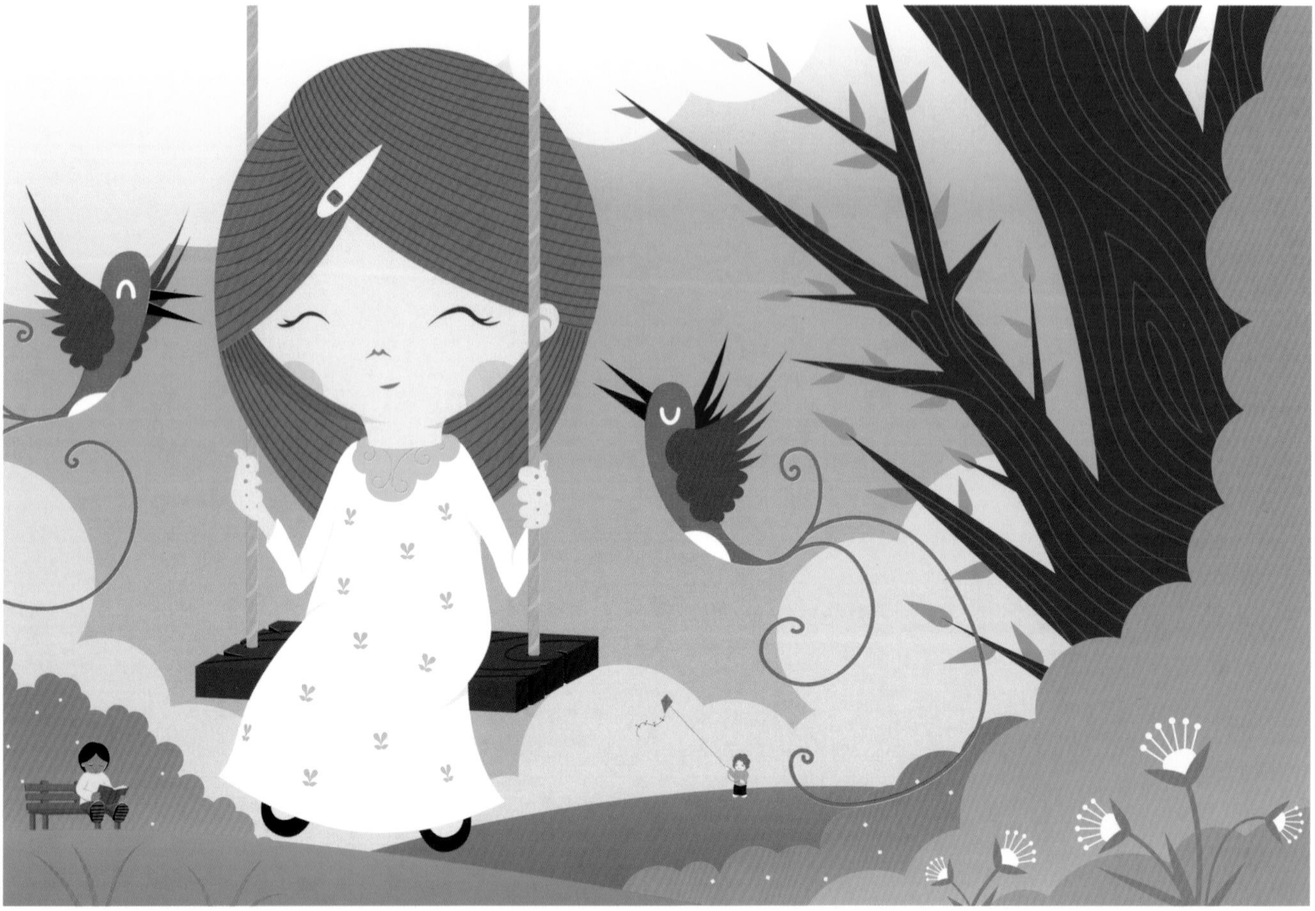

owen rimington | advocate-art.com

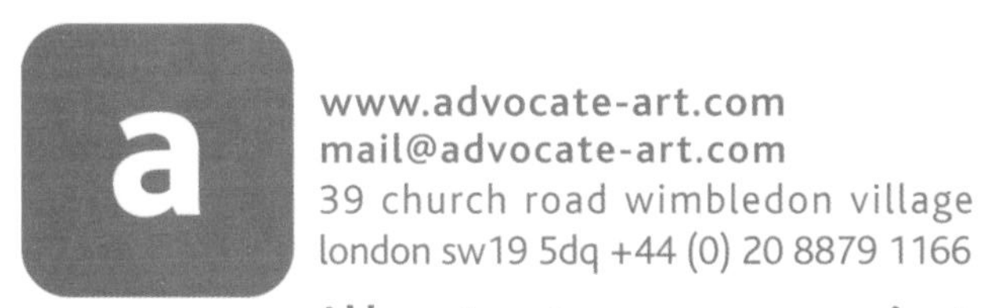

pablo pasadas | advocate-art.com

peter mac | advocate-art.com

arenaworks.com

0845 050 7600 info@arenaworks.com

SUSAN HELLARD

TERESA MURFIN

TERESA MURFIN

Fabulous Tales
BOO!
BOO
HAVE A GO IF YOU THINK YOU'RE HARD ENOUGH!

STEVE MAY

THE GREATEST SHOW ON EARTH
CIRCUS
NEW FEATURES Larger THAN EVER

DAVID HITCH

DAVID HITCH

arenaworks.com

0845 050 7600 info@arenaworks.com

DAVID HITCH

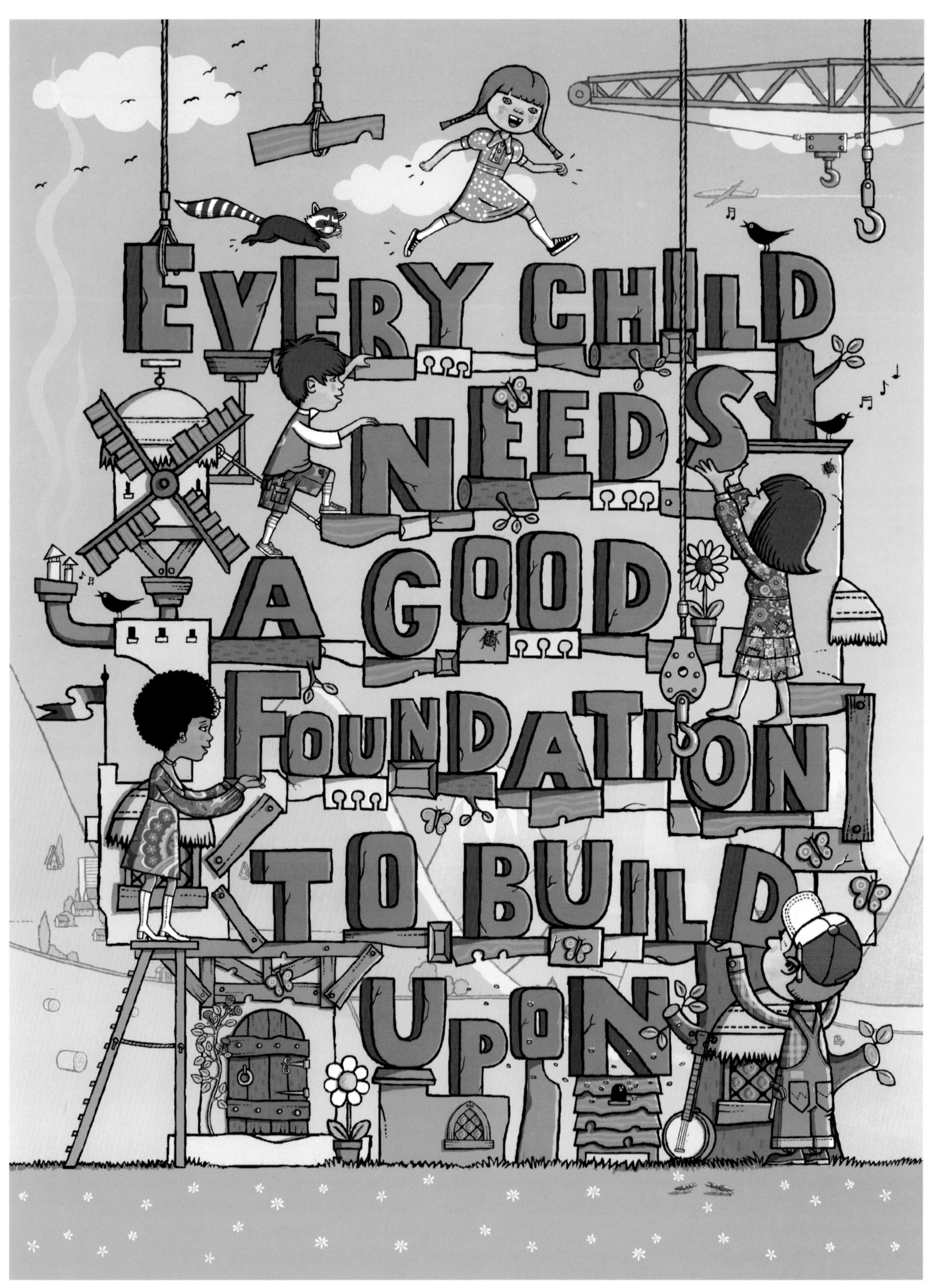

FRANCES CASTLE

arenaworks.com

0845 050 7600 info@arenaworks.com

CHRIS GARBUTT

CHRISTOPHER GIBBS

JOHN HOWE

DOMINIC HARMAN

artist **partners ltd**

Contact: Christine Isteed, 2E The Chandlery, 50 Westminster Bridge Road, London SEI 7QY
T: +44 (0) 20 7401 7904 *F:* +44 (0) 20 7401 3378 *E:* christine@artistpartners.com

Earlier this year Artist Partners relocated south of the river, where in 1951 its artists and designers were involved in the works and exhibition of The Festival of Britain - Now surrounded and intoxicated by the creative presence of the South Bank, Artist Partners continues with renewed vigour. *Christine Isteed*

Cover illustration David Frankland. Index page David Roberts. Brochure design by Bruno Tilley.

artist partners ltd

Contact: Christine Isteed, 2E The Chandlery, 50 Westminster Bridge Road, London SEI 7QY
T: +44 (0) 20 7401 7904 F: +44 (0) 20 7401 3378 E: christine@artistpartners.com

AARON ROBINSON

www.artistpartners.com

artist partners ltd

Contact: Christine Isteed, 2E The Chandlery, 50 Westminster Bridge Road, London SEI 7QY
T: +44 (0) 20 7401 7904 F: +44 (0) 20 7401 3378 E: christine@artistpartners.com

ANGELO RINALDI

www.artistpartners.com

Contact: Christine Isteed, 2E The Chandlery, 50 Westminster Bridge Road, London SEI 7QY
T: +44 (0) 20 7401 7904 F: +44 (0) 20 7401 3378 E: christine@artistpartners.com

ANGELO RINALDI

www.artistpartners.com

Contact: Christine Isteed, 2E The Chandlery, 50 Westminster Bridge Road, London SEI 7QY
T: +44 (0) 20 7401 7904 *F:* +44 (0) 20 7401 3378 *E:* christine@artistpartners.com

RICHARD JONES

www.artistpartners.com

Contact: Christine Isteed, 2E The Chandlery, 50 Westminster Bridge Road, London SEI 7QY
T: +44 (0) 20 7401 7904 F: +44 (0) 20 7401 3378 E: christine@artistpartners.com

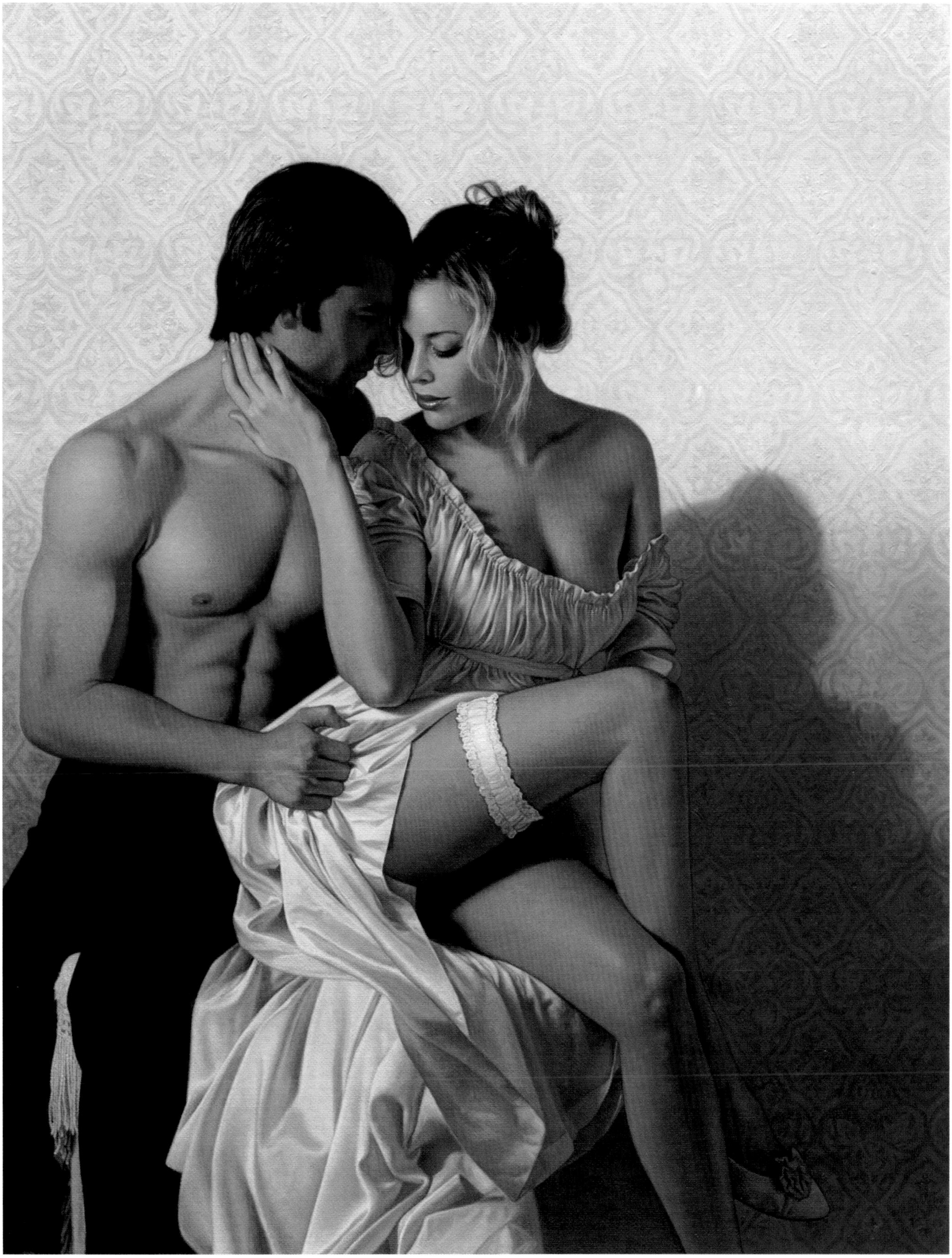

RICHARD JONES

www.artistpartners.com

artist partners ltd

Contact: Christine Isteed, 2E The Chandlery, 50 Westminster Bridge Road, London SEI 7QY
T: +44 (0) 20 7401 7904 F: +44 (0) 20 7401 3378 E: christine@artistpartners.com

GWYNETH JONES

www.artistpartners.com

artist **partners ltd**

Contact: Christine Isteed, 2E The Chandlery, 50 Westminster Bridge Road, London SEI 7QY
T: +44 (0) 20 7401 7904 F: +44 (0) 20 7401 3378 E: christine@artistpartners.com

GWYNETH JONES

www.artistpartners.com

artist partners ltd

Contact: Christine Isteed, 2E The Chandlery, 50 Westminster Bridge Road, London SEI 7QY
T: +44 (0) 20 7401 7904 F: +44 (0) 20 7401 3378 E: christine@artistpartners.com

ROD HOLT

www.artistpartners.com

artist **partners ltd**

Contact: Christine Isteed, 2E The Chandlery, 50 Westminster Bridge Road, London SEI 7QY
T: +44 (0) 20 7401 7904 *F:* +44 (0) 20 7401 3378 *E:* christine@artistpartners.com

MARK EDWARDS

www.artistpartners.com

artist partners ltd

Contact: Christine Isteed, 2E The Chandlery, 50 Westminster Bridge Road, London SEI 7QY
T: +44 (0) 20 7401 7904 F: +44 (0) 20 7401 3378 E: christine@artistpartners.com

SAM HADLEY

artist partners ltd

Contact: Christine Isteed, 2E The Chandlery, 50 Westminster Bridge Road, London SEI 7QY
T: +44 (0) 20 7401 7904 F: +44 (0) 20 7401 3378 E: christine@artistpartners.com

SAM HADLEY

Contact: Christine Isteed, 2E The Chandlery, 50 Westminster Bridge Road, London SEI 7QY
T: +44 (0) 20 7401 7904 *F:* +44 (0) 20 7401 3378 *E:* christine@artistpartners.com

PAUL YOUNG

www.artistpartners.com

artist partners ltd
Contact: Christine Isteed, 2E The Chandlery, 50 Westminster Bridge Road, London SEI 7QY
T: +44 (0) 20 7401 7904 F: +44 (0) 20 7401 3378 E: christine@artistpartners.com

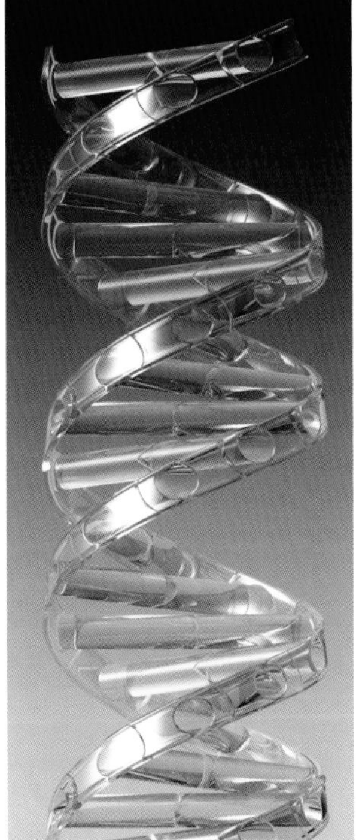

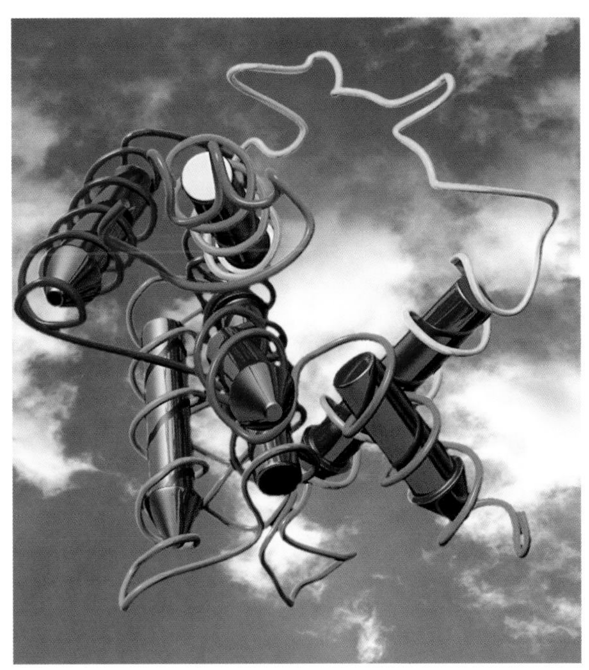

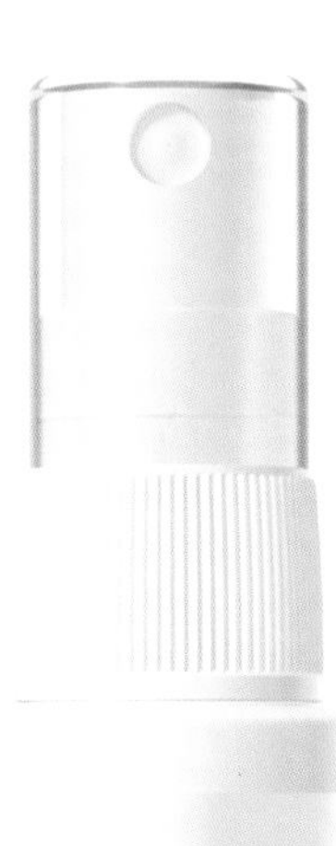

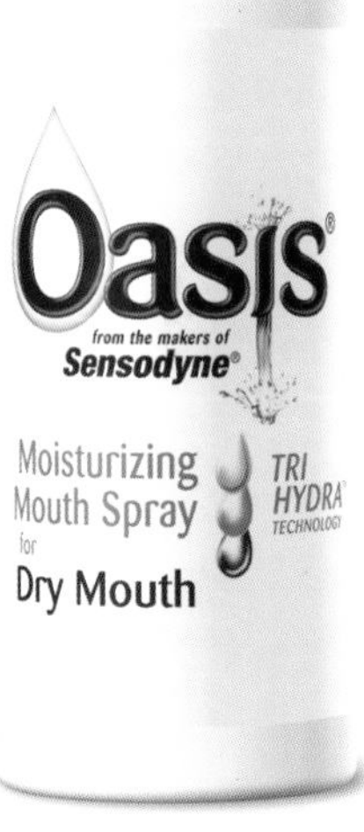

JOHN HARWOOD

www.artistpartners.com

artist partners ltd

Contact: Christine Isteed, 2E The Chandlery, 50 Westminster Bridge Road, London SEI 7QY
T: +44 (0) 20 7401 7904 F: +44 (0) 20 7401 3378 E: christine@artistpartners.com

STEVE STONE

www.artistpartners.com

Contact: Christine Isteed, 2E The Chandlery, 50 Westminster Bridge Road, London SE1 7QY
T: +44 (0) 20 7401 7904 F: +44 (0) 20 7401 3378 E: christine@artistpartners.com

'A brilliant, fast-paced epic, bringing an entire people back to roaring life. Superb.'
CONN IGGULDEN

SAM BARONE

Empire Rising

STEVE STONE

www.artistpartners.com

artist partners ltd

Contact: Christine Isteed, 2E The Chandlery, 50 Westminster Bridge Road, London SEI 7QY
T: +44 (0) 20 7401 7904 F: +44 (0) 20 7401 3378 E: christine@artistpartners.com

CHRIS MOORE

www.artistpartners.com

Contact: Christine Isteed, 2E The Chandlery, 50 Westminster Bridge Road, London SEI 7QY
T: +44 (0) 20 7401 7904 F: +44 (0) 20 7401 3378 E: christine@artistpartners.com

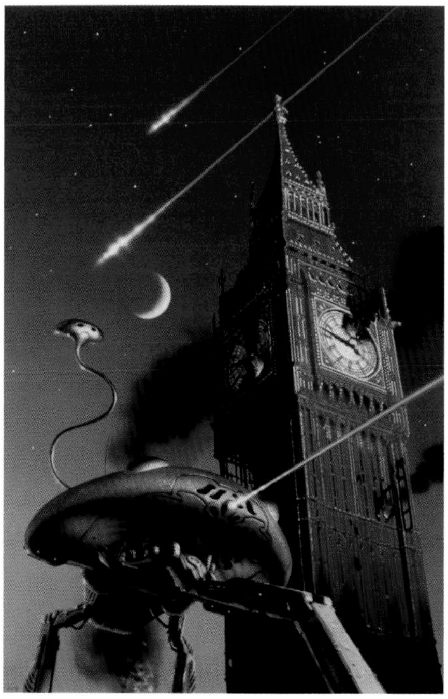

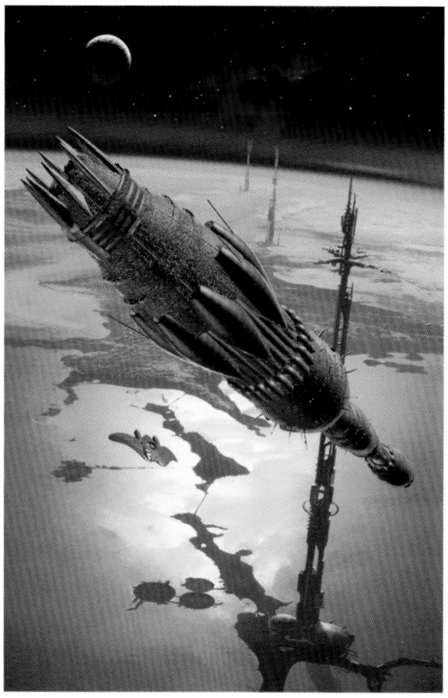

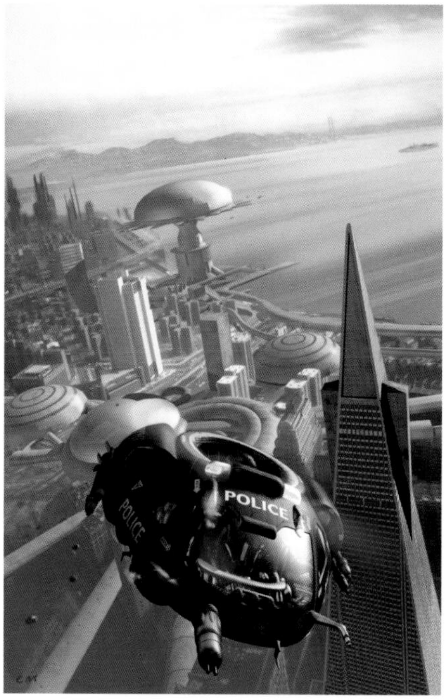

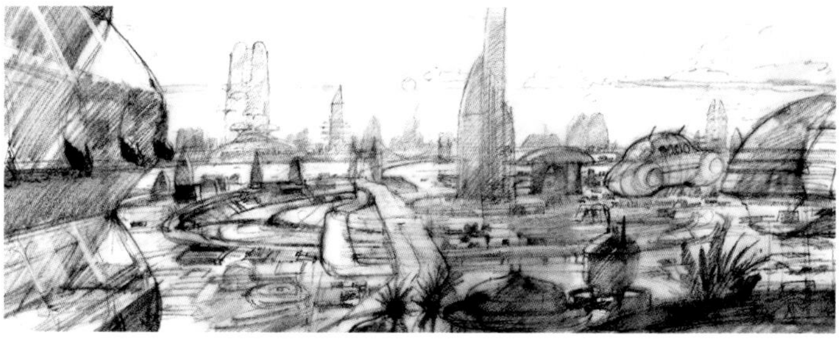

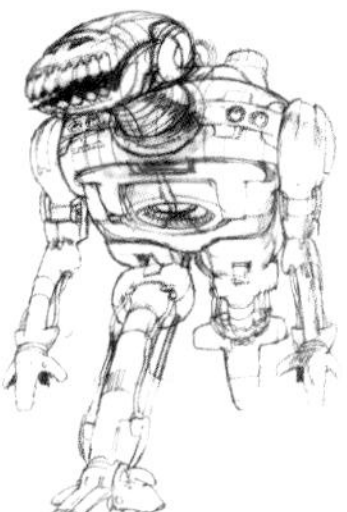

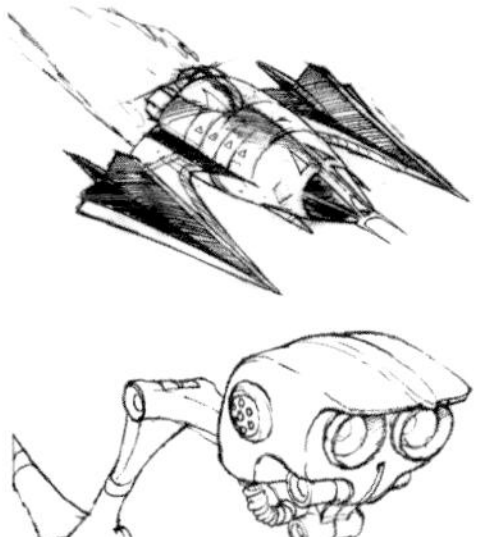

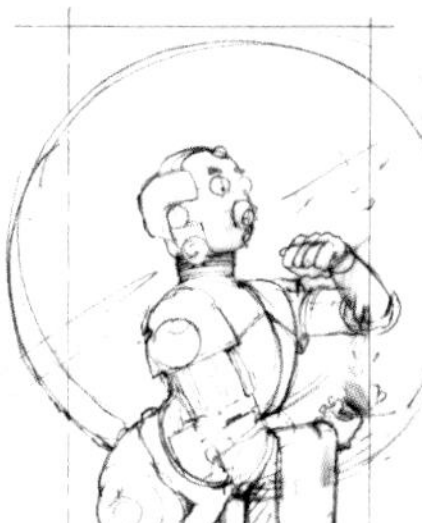

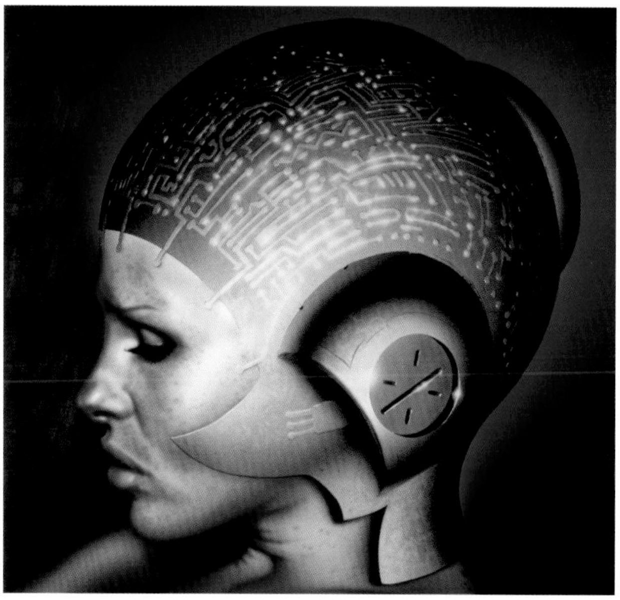

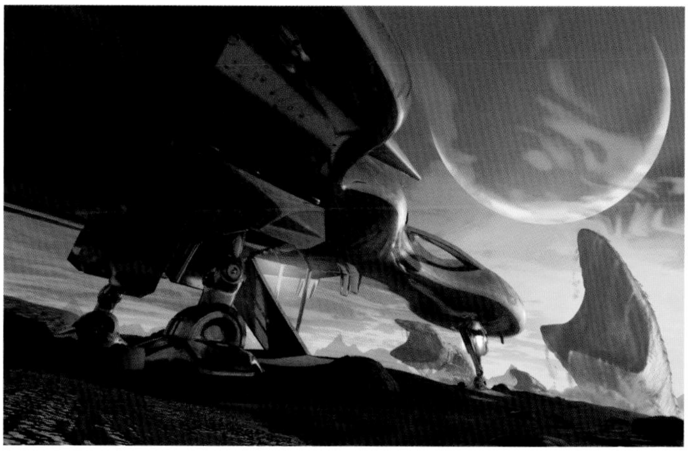

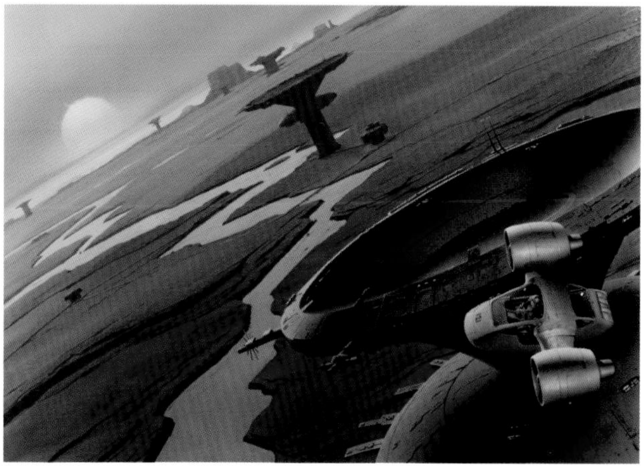

CHRIS MOORE

www.artistpartners.com

artist partners ltd

Contact: Christine Isteed, 2E The Chandlery, 50 Westminster Bridge Road, London SEI 7QY
T: +44 (0) 20 7401 7904 F: +44 (0) 20 7401 3378 E: christine@artistpartners.com

LARRY ROSTANT

www.artistpartners.com

artist partners ltd

Contact: Christine Isteed, 2E The Chandlery, 50 Westminster Bridge Road, London SEI 7QY
T: +44 (0) 20 7401 7904 F: +44 (0) 20 7401 3378 E: christine@artistpartners.com

LARRY ROSTANT

www.artistpartners.com

artist partners ltd

Contact: Christine Isteed, 2E The Chandlery, 50 Westminster Bridge Road, London SEI 7QY
T: +44 (0) 20 7401 7904 F: +44 (0) 20 7401 3378 E: christine@artistpartners.com

DAVID FRANKLAND

www.artistpartners.com

Contact: Christine Isteed, 2E The Chandlery, 50 Westminster Bridge Road, London SE1 7QY
T: +44 (0) 20 7401 7904 *F:* +44 (0) 20 7401 3378 *E:* christine@artistpartners.com

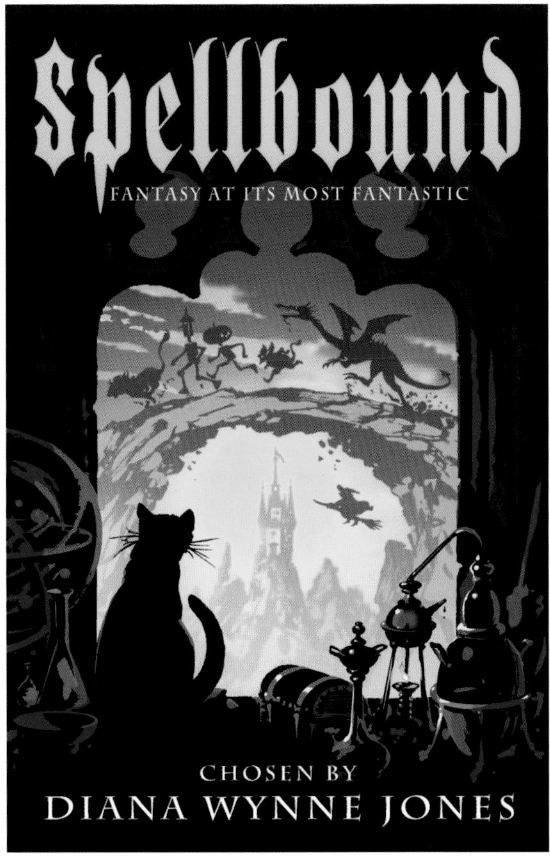

DAVID FRANKLAND

artist partners ltd

Contact: Christine Isteed, 2E The Chandlery, 50 Westminster Bridge Road, London SEI 7QY
T: +44 (0) 20 7401 7904 *F:* +44 (0) 20 7401 3378 *E:* christine@artistpartners.com

BRIAN SANDERS

LIZZIE SANDERS

www.artistpartners.com

Contact: Christine Isteed, 2E The Chandlery, 50 Westminster Bridge Road, London SE1 7QY
T: +44 (0) 20 7401 7904 F: +44 (0) 20 7401 3378 E: christine@artistpartners.com

LAUREN BISHOP

www.artistpartners.com

Contact: Christine Isteed, 2E The Chandlery, 50 Westminster Bridge Road, London SEI 7QY
T: +44 (0) 20 7401 7904 *F:* +44 (0) 20 7401 3378 *E:* christine@artistpartners.com

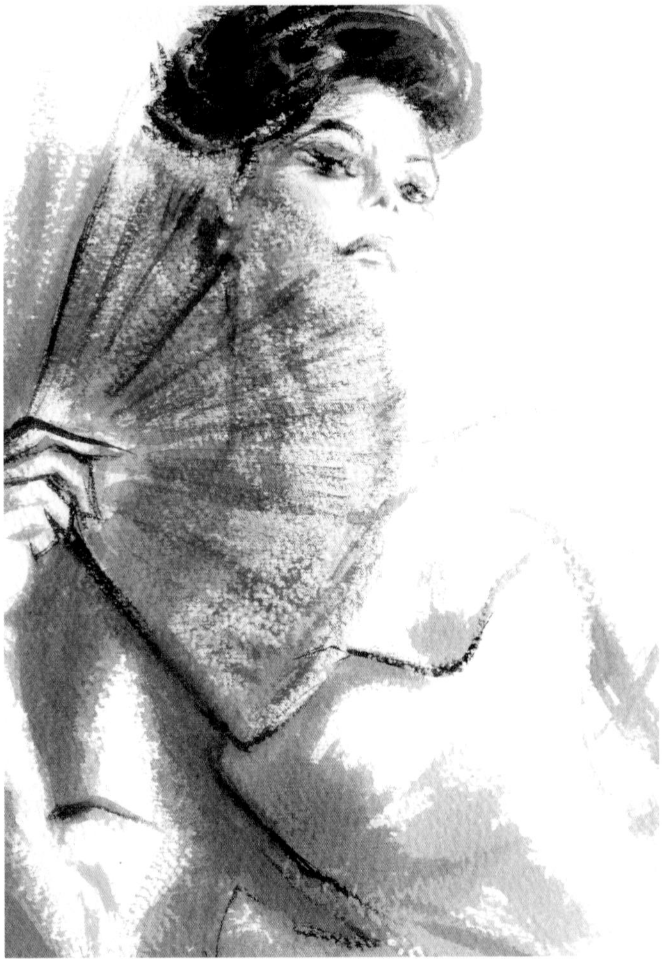

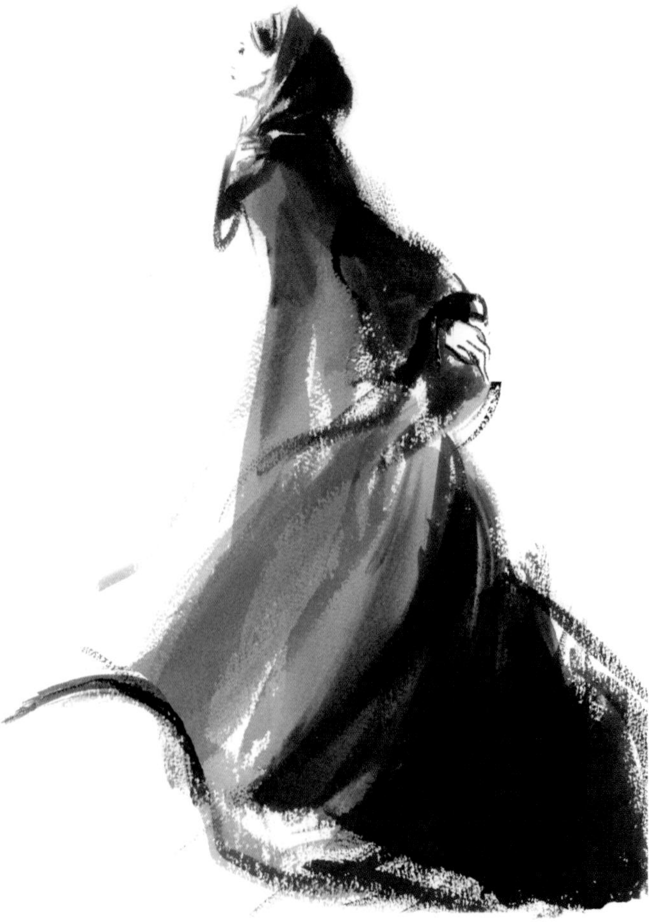

SHARON PINSKER

www.artistpartners.com

artist partners ltd

Contact: Christine Isteed, 2E The Chandlery, 50 Westminster Bridge Road, London SEI 7QY
T: +44 (0) 20 7401 7904 F: +44 (0) 20 7401 3378 E: christine@artistpartners.com

SHARON PINSKER

www.artistpartners.com

Contact: Christine Isteed, 2E The Chandlery, 50 Westminster Bridge Road, London SEI 7QY
T: +44 (0) 20 7401 7904 *F:* +44 (0) 20 7401 3378 *E:* christine@artistpartners.com

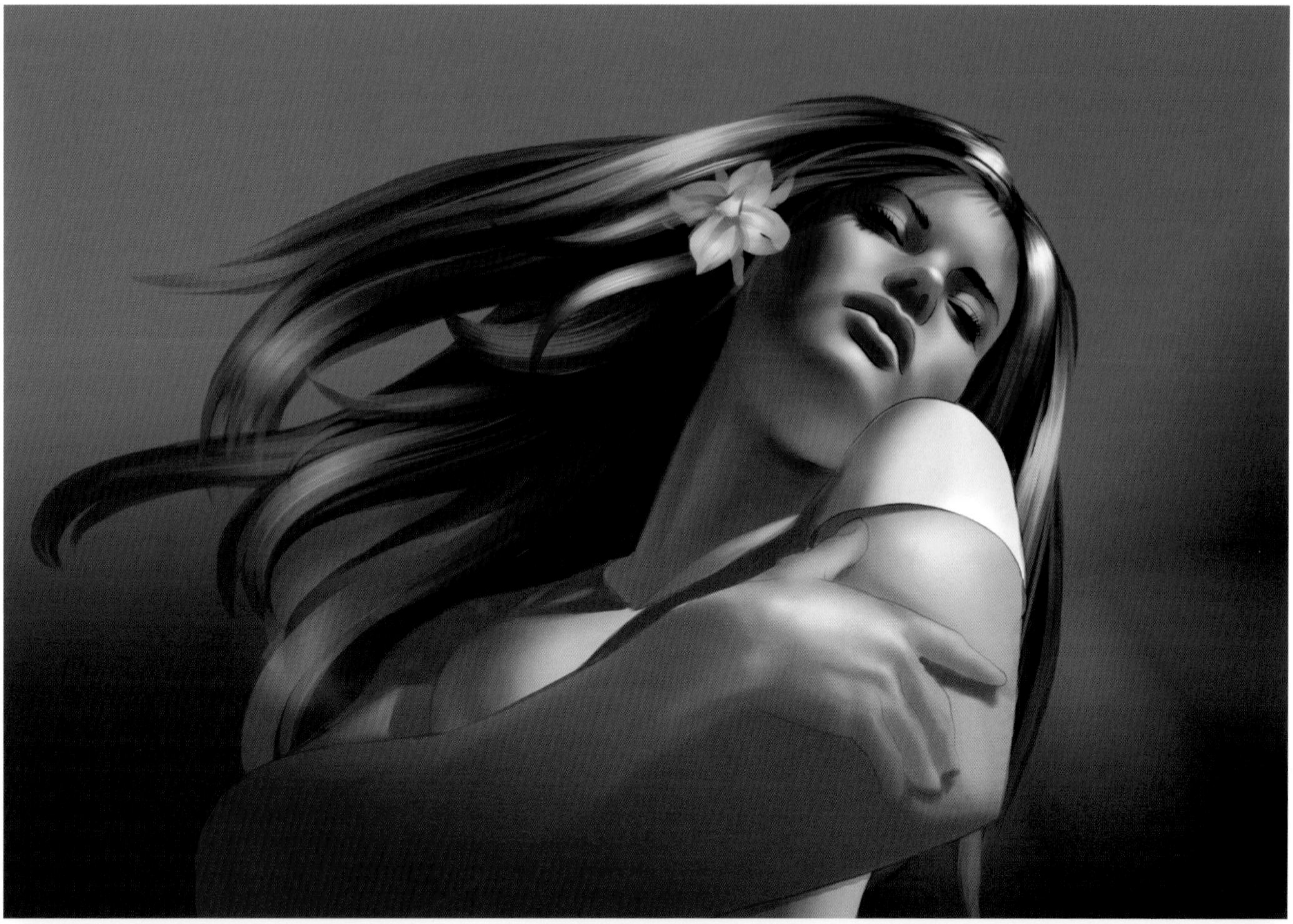

ADAM WILLIS

www.artistpartners.com

artist partners ltd

Contact: Christine Isteed, 2E The Chandlery, 50 Westminster Bridge Road, London SE1 7QY
T: +44 (0) 20 7401 7904 F: +44 (0) 20 7401 3378 E: christine@artistpartners.com

ADAM WILLIS

www.artistpartners.com

Contact: Christine Isteed, 2E The Chandlery, 50 Westminster Bridge Road, London SEI 7QY
T: +44 (0) 20 7401 7904 *F:* +44 (0) 20 7401 3378 *E:* christine@artistpartners.com

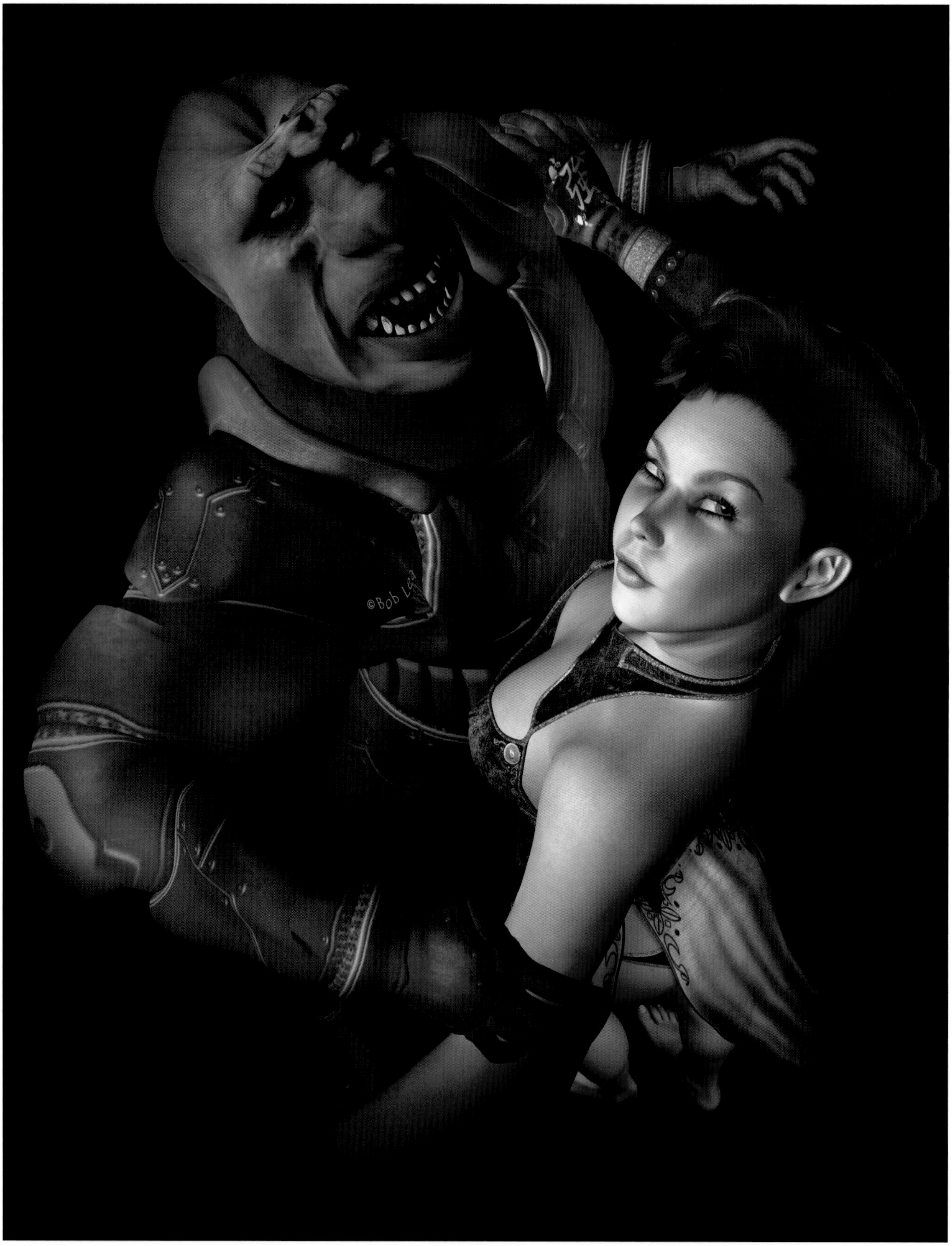

BOB LEA

www.artistpartners.com

artist partners ltd

Contact: Christine Isteed, 2E The Chandlery, 50 Westminster Bridge Road, London SEI 7QY
T: +44 (0) 20 7401 7904 F: +44 (0) 20 7401 3378 E: christine@artistpartners.com

BOB LEA

www.artistpartners.com

Contact: Christine Isteed, 2E The Chandlery, 50 Westminster Bridge Road, London SEI 7QY
T: +44 (0) 20 7401 7904 F: +44 (0) 20 7401 3378 E: christine@artistpartners.com

MEL GRANT

www.artistpartners.com

Contact: Christine Isteed, 2E The Chandlery, 50 Westminster Bridge Road, London SEI 7QY
T: +44 (0) 20 7401 7904 F: +44 (0) 20 7401 3378 E: christine@artistpartners.com

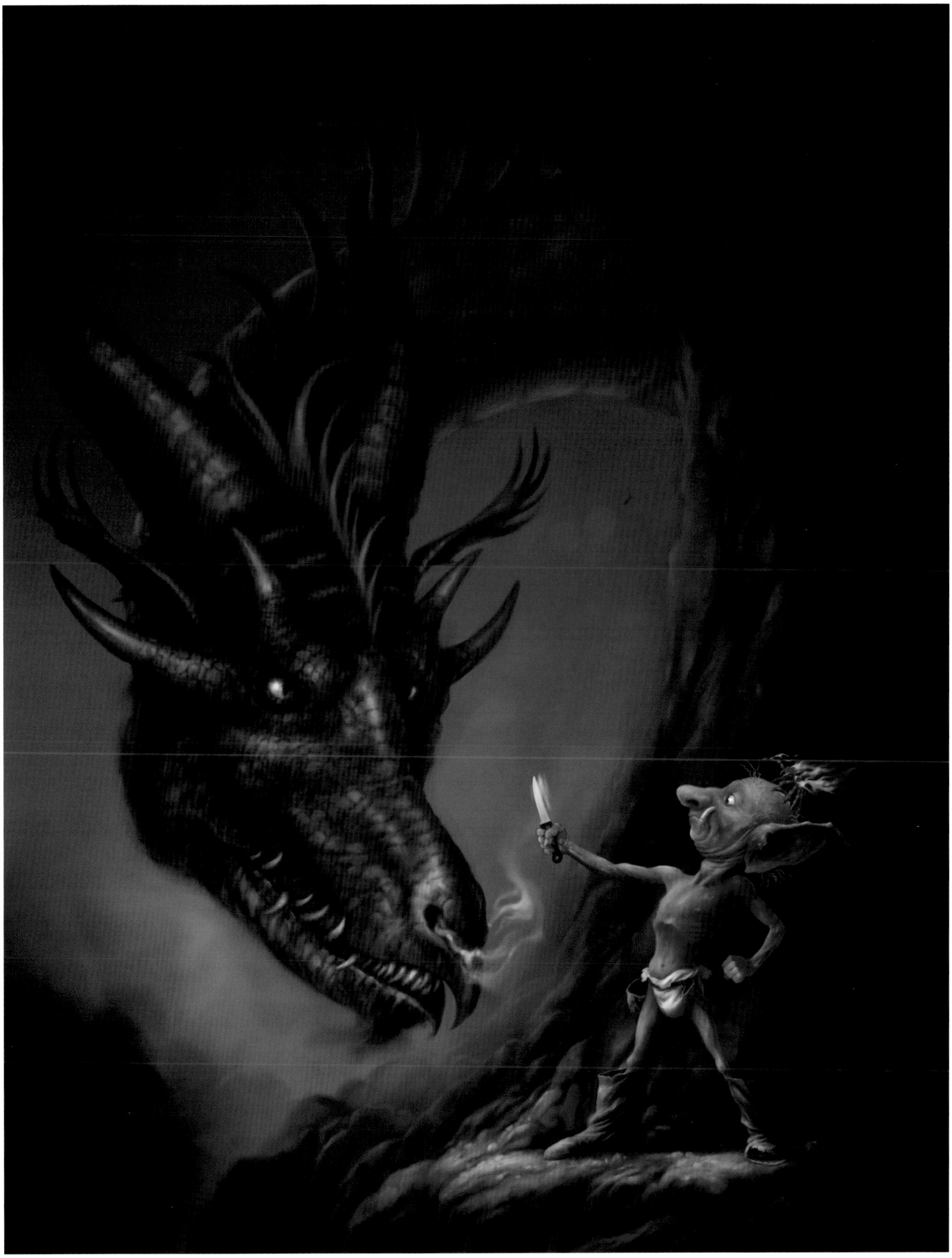

MEL GRANT

artist partners ltd

Contact: Christine Isteed, 2E The Chandlery, 50 Westminster Bridge Road, London SEI 7QY
T: +44 (0) 20 7401 7904 *F:* +44 (0) 20 7401 3378 *E:* christine@artistpartners.com

GARY BLYTHE

Contact: Christine Isteed, 2E The Chandlery, 50 Westminster Bridge Road, London SEI 7QY
T: +44 (0) 20 7401 7904 F: +44 (0) 20 7401 3378 E: christine@artistpartners.com

GARY BLYTHE

www.artistpartners.com

artist partners ltd

Contact: Christine Isteed, 2E The Chandlery, 50 Westminster Bridge Road, London SEI 7QY
T: +44 (0) 20 7401 7904 *F:* +44 (0) 20 7401 3378 *E:* christine@artistpartners.com

KAYE HODGES

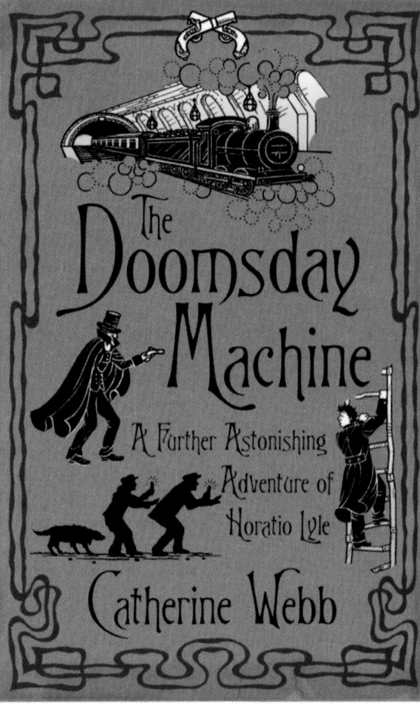

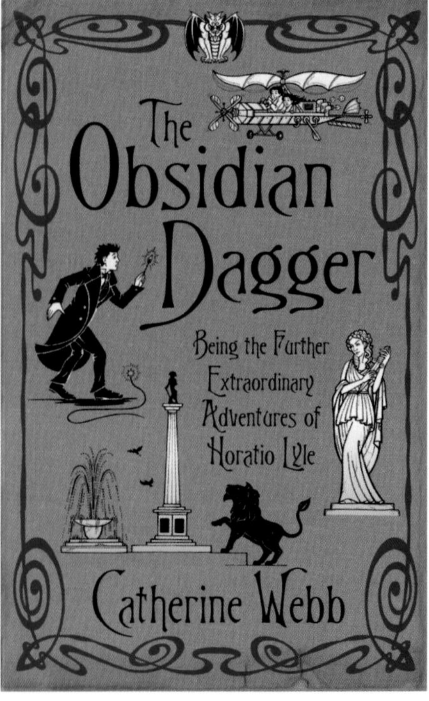

SALLY TAYLOR

artist partners ltd

Contact: Christine Isteed, 2E The Chandlery, 50 Westminster Bridge Road, London SEI 7QY
T: +44 (0) 20 7401 7904 F: +44 (0) 20 7401 3378 E: christine@artistpartners.com

STEPHEN PLAYER

www.artistpartners.com

artist partners ltd

Contact: Christine Isteed, 2E The Chandlery, 50 Westminster Bridge Road, London SEI 7QY
T: +44 (0) 20 7401 7904 F: +44 (0) 20 7401 3378 E: christine@artistpartners.com

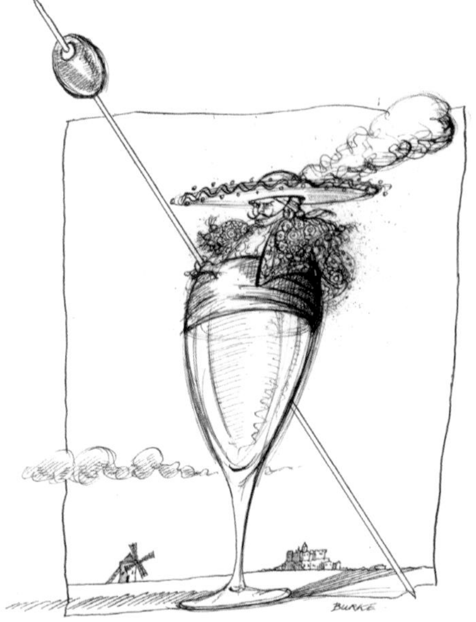

CHRIS BURKE

www.artistpartners.com

artist partners ltd

Contact: Christine Isteed, 2E The Chandlery, 50 Westminster Bridge Road, London SEI 7QY
T: +44 (0) 20 7401 7904 F: +44 (0) 20 7401 3378 E: christine@artistpartners.com

MAX SCHINDLER - Pastiche Artist

artist **partners ltd**

Contact: Christine Isteed, 2E The Chandlery, 50 Westminster Bridge Road, London SEI 7QY
T: +44 (0) 20 7401 7904 *F:* +44 (0) 20 7401 3378 *E:* christine@artistpartners.com

CAPTAIN SAFARI

GINO D'ACHILLE

www.artistpartners.com

CIA
La French
12 FOOT 6 . ALAN ALDRIDGE .
TOM BAGSHAW . ANDREW BANNECKER . JONAS BERGSTRAND . BERTIE BIB . IAN BILBEY .
SIR PETER BLAKE . BERNARD BLATCH . STEPHEN BLISS . LOUISE BRIERLEY . CHRISTOPHER BROWN . MICK BROWNFIELD .
LESLEY BUCKINGHAM . SUSAN BURGHART . LEONELLO CALVETTI . STANLEY CHOW . NISHANT CHOKSI . HAYDN CORNNER .
DUST . TRISTAN EATON . MAX ELLIS . JEFF FISHER . JESSIE FORD . ANDREW FOSTER . JONATHAN GIBBS .
CHRIS GILVAN CARTWRIGHT . BRIAN GRIMWOOD . MARTIN HAAKE . OLAF HAJEK . TOMER HANUKA . JOHNNY HARDSTAFF .
SARA HAYWARD . HELLOVON . FINE & DANDY . DAVID HOLMES . DARREN HOPES . PETER HORRIDGE . DAVID HUGHES .
THORBJORN INGASON . M. H. JEEVES . ADRIAN JOHNSON . KAI & SUNNY . CHRIS KASCH . LA FRENCH .
CAROL LAWSON . JIMI MACKAY . JACQUELINE MAIR . TINA MANSUWAN . TIM MARRS . MICK MARSTON . CHRIS MCEWAN .
MCFAUL . CLARE MELINSKY . KATE MILLER . DAVE NEEDHAM . FABIAN NEGRIN . GARY NEILL . PAUL OAKLEY .
KRISTIAN OLSON . NIGEL OWEN . JACKIE PARSONS . JITESH PATEL . WENDY PLOVMAND . ULLA PUGGAARD .
MARIA RAYMONDSDOTTER . JOHN ROYLE . HARRIET RUSSELL . JEREMY SANCHA . PAUL SLATER . RAY SMITH .
JOHN SPENCER . SIMON SPILSBURY . SPIRAL STUDIO . LOUISA ST. PIERRE . SYMBOLON . MARK THOMAS .
BENJAMIN WACHENJE . RUSSELL WALKER . PAUL WEARING .
RICHARD WILKINSON . MIKE WILKS . YUKO .
WWW.CENTRALILLUSTRATION.COM
LONDON, NEW YORK, DUBAI, SHANGHAI, BARCELONA

Central Illustration Agency
36 Wellington Street
Covent Garden
London, UK, WC2E 7BD

T: +44(0)20 7240 8925
F: +44(0)20 7836 1177
info@centralillustration.com
www.centralillustration.com

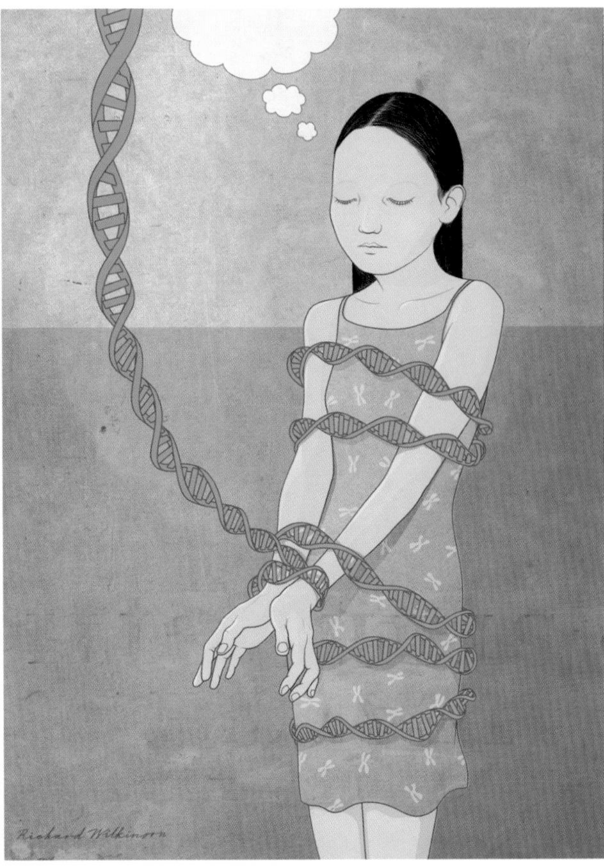

RICHARD WILKINSON

www.centralillustration.com

Central Illustration Agency
36 Wellington Street
Covent Garden
London, UK, WC2E 7BD

T: +44(0)20 7240 8925
F: +44(0)20 7836 1177
info@centralillustration.com
www.centralillustration.com

BRIAN GRIMWOOD

www.centralillustration.com

Central Illustration Agency
36 Wellington Street
Covent Garden
London, UK, WC2E 7BD

T: +44(0)20 7240 8925
F: +44(0)20 7836 1177
info@centralillustration.com
www.centralillustration.com

BRIAN GRIMWOOD

www.centralillustration.com

Central Illustration Agency
36 Wellington Street
Covent Garden
London, UK, WC2E 7BD

T: +44(0)20 7240 8925
F: +44(0)20 7836 1177
info@centralillustration.com
www.centralillustration.com

TOM BAGSHAW

www.centralillustration.com

Central Illustration Agency
36 Wellington Street
Covent Garden
London, UK, WC2E 7BD

T: +44(0)20 7240 8925
F: +44(0)20 7836 1177
info@centralillustration.com
www.centralillustration.com

DARREN HOPES

www.centralillustration.com

Central Illustration Agency
36 Wellington Street
Covent Garden
London, UK, WC2E 7BD

T: +44(0)20 7240 8925
F: +44(0)20 7836 1177
info@centralillustration.com
www.centralillustration.com

ADRIAN JOHNSON

www.centralillustration.com

Central Illustration Agency
36 Wellington Street
Covent Garden
London, UK, WC2E 7BD

T: +44(0)20 7240 8925
F: +44(0)20 7836 1177
info@centralillustration.com
www.centralillustration.com

RAISE THEM ON ROBINSONS®

NO ARTIFICIAL COLOURS OR FLAVOURS

ADRIAN JOHNSON

www.centralillustration.com

Central Illustration Agency
36 Wellington Street
Covent Garden
London, UK, WC2E 7BD

T: +44(0)20 7240 8925
F: +44(0)20 7836 1177
info@centralillustration.com
www.centralillustration.com

STAN CHOW

www.centralillustration.com

Central Illustration Agency
36 Wellington Street
Covent Garden
London, UK, WC2E 7BD

T: +44(0)20 7240 8925
F: +44(0)20 7836 1177
info@centralillustration.com
www.centralillustration.com

NISHANT CHOKSI

www.centralillustration.com

Central Illustration Agency
36 Wellington Street
Covent Garden
London, UK, WC2E 7BD

T: +44(0)20 7240 8925
F: +44(0)20 7836 1177
info@centralillustration.com
www.centralillustration.com

MCFAUL

www.centralillustration.com

Central Illustration Agency
36 Wellington Street
Covent Garden
London, UK, WC2E 7BD

T: +44(0)20 7240 8925
F: +44(0)20 7836 1177
info@centralillustration.com
www.centralillustration.com

photography http://www.lezliandrose.com 

MCFAUL

www.centralillustration.com

Central Illustration Agency
36 Wellington Street
Covent Garden
London, UK, WC2E 7BD

T: +44(0)20 7240 8925
F: +44(0)20 7836 1177
info@centralillustration.com
www.centralillustration.com

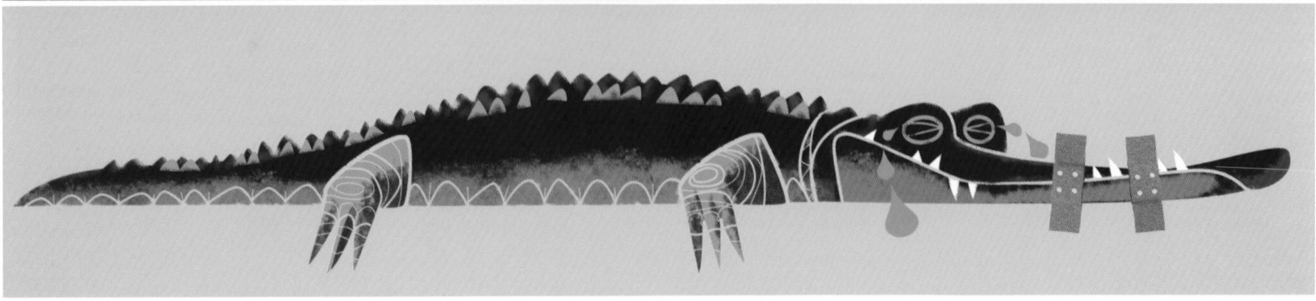

JONAS BERGSTRAND

www.centralillustration.com

Central Illustration Agency
36 Wellington Street
Covent Garden
London, UK, WC2E 7BD

T: +44(0)20 7240 8925
F: +44(0)20 7836 1177
info@centralillustration.com
www.centralillustration.com

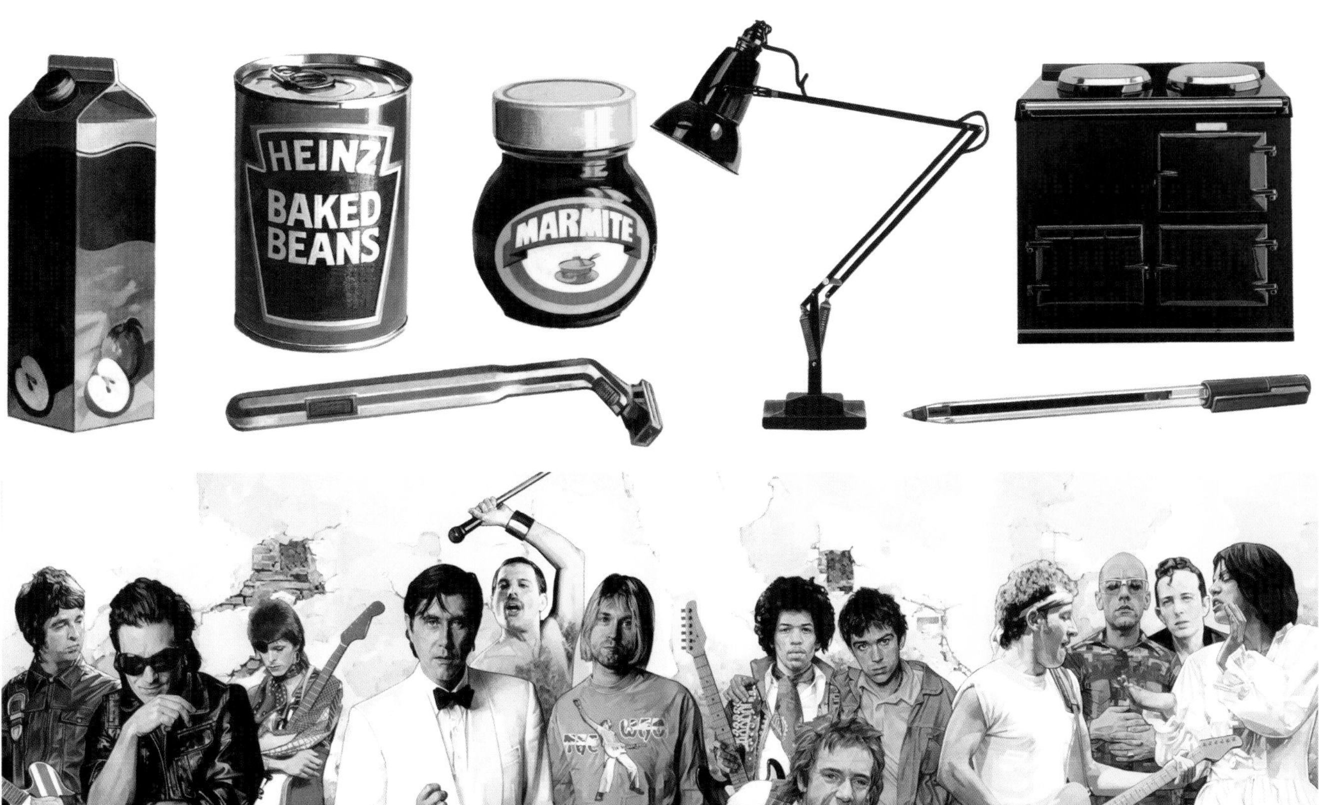

CHRIS KASCH

Central Illustration Agency
36 Wellington Street
Covent Garden
London, UK, WC2E 7BD

T: +44(0)20 7240 8925
F: +44(0)20 7836 1177
info@centralillustration.com
www.centralillustration.com

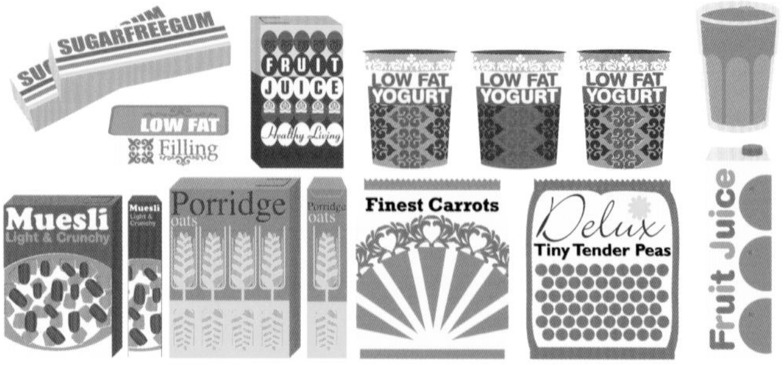

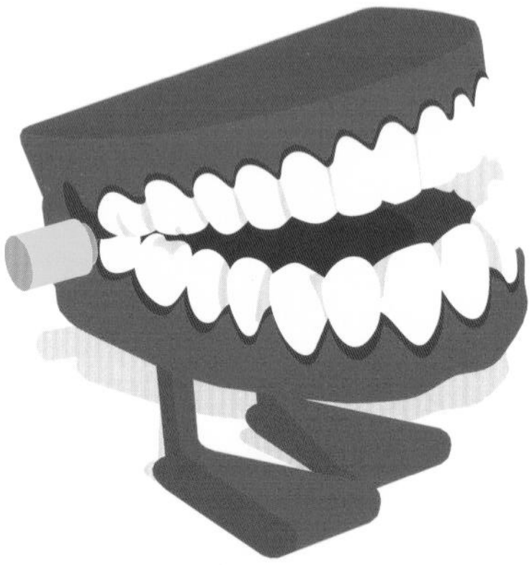

IAN BILBEY

Central Illustration Agency
36 Wellington Street
Covent Garden
London, UK, WC2E 7BD

T: +44(0)20 7240 8925
F: +44(0)20 7836 1177
info@centralillustration.com
www.centralillustration.com

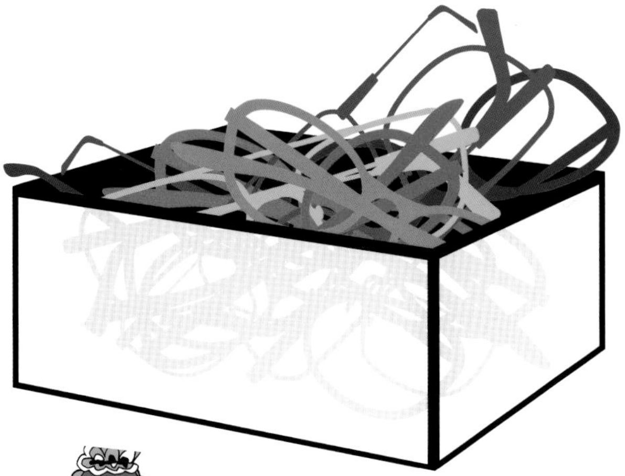

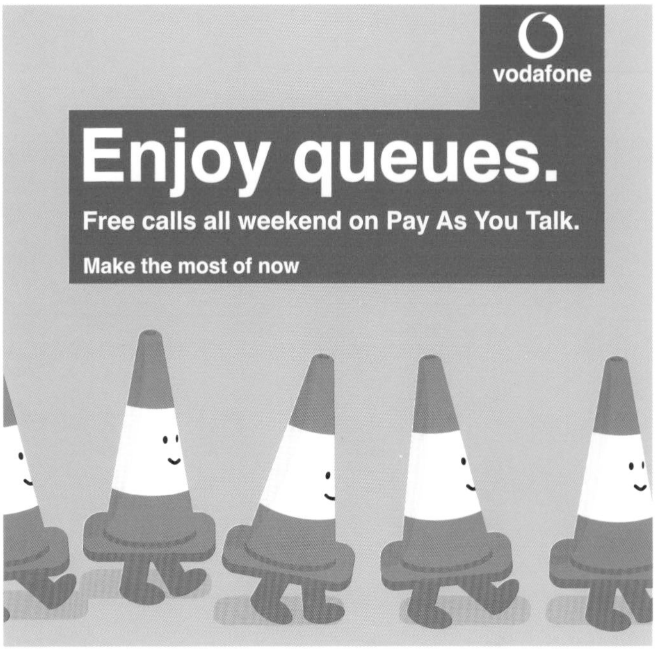

vodafone
Enjoy queues.
Free calls all weekend on Pay As You Talk.
Make the most of now

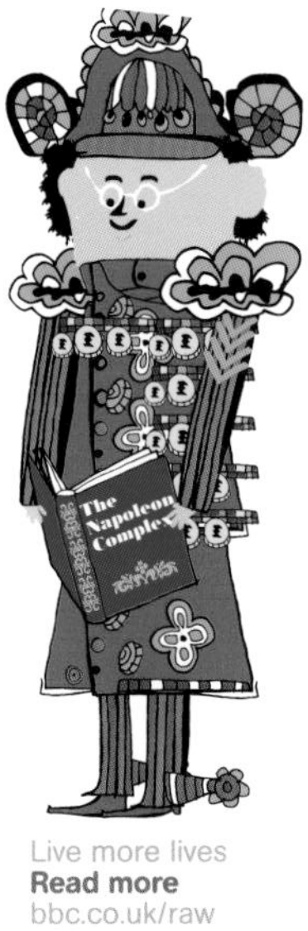

ianbilbey.com

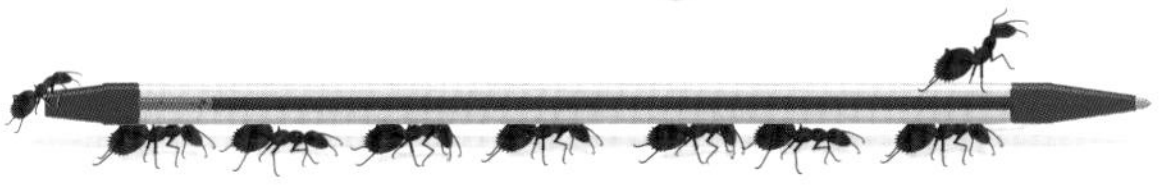

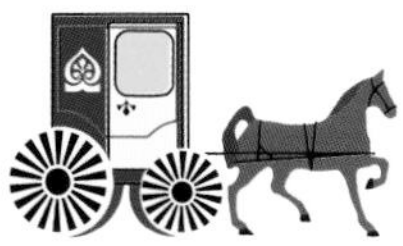

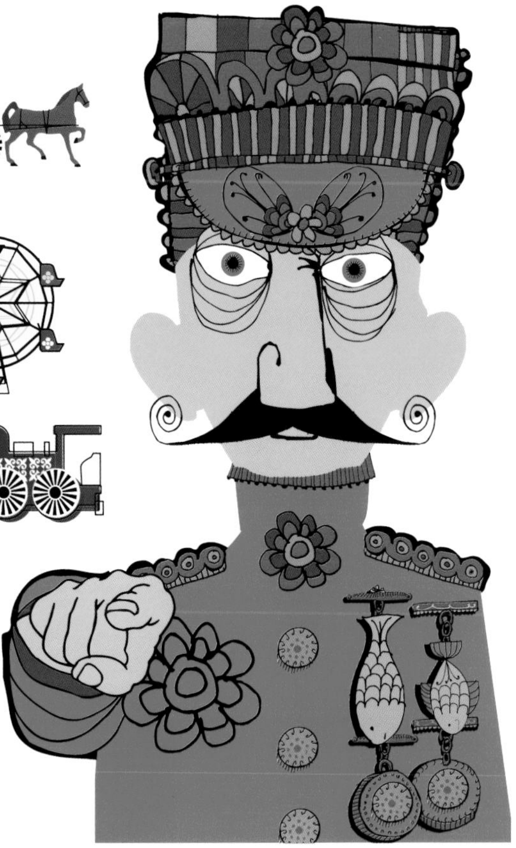

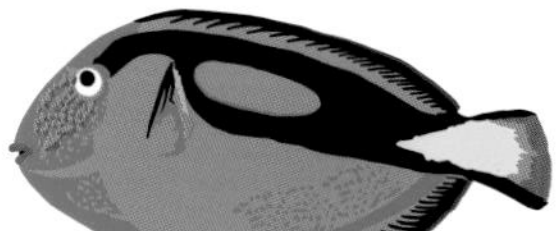

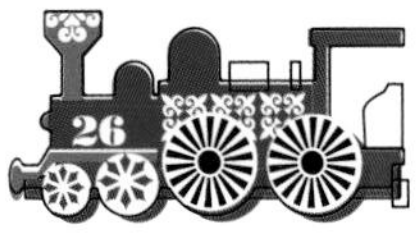

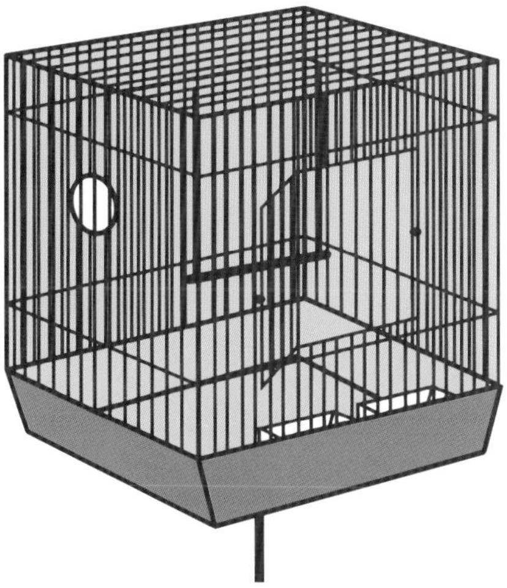

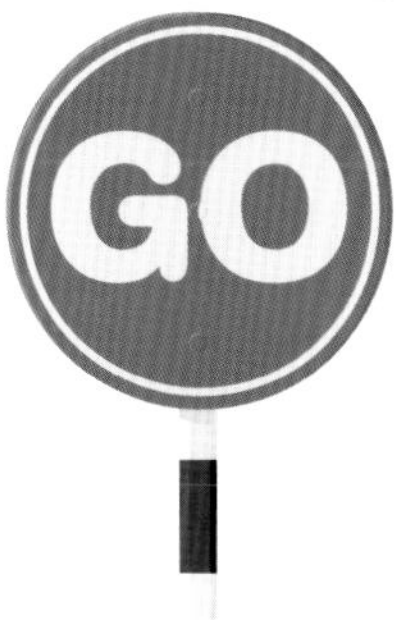

Live more lives
Read more
bbc.co.uk/raw

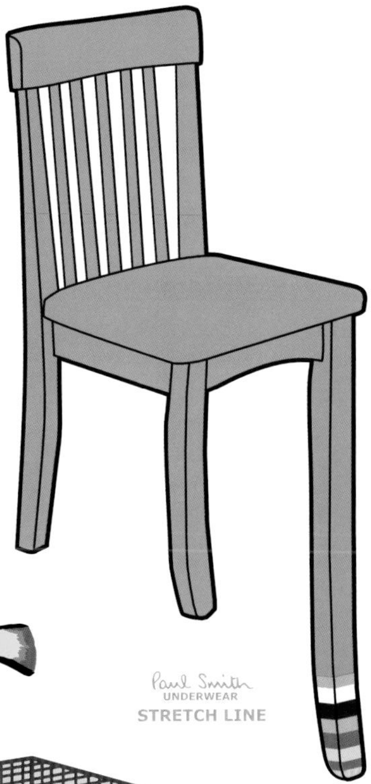

Paul Smith
UNDERWEAR
STRETCH LINE

GO

IAN BILBEY

Central Illustration Agency
36 Wellington Street
Covent Garden
London, UK, WC2E 7BD

T: +44(0)20 7240 8925
F: +44(0)20 7836 1177
info@centralillustration.com
www.centralillustration.com

SPIRAL STUDIO

Central Illustration Agency
36 Wellington Street
Covent Garden
London, UK, WC2E 7BD

T: +44(0)20 7240 8925
F: +44(0)20 7836 1177
info@centralillustration.com
www.centralillustration.com

MARIA RAYMONDSDOTTER

www.centralillustration.com

Central Illustration Agency
36 Wellington Street
Covent Garden
London, UK, WC2E 7BD

T: +44(0)20 7240 8925
F: +44(0)20 7836 1177
info@centralillustration.com
www.centralillustration.com

BENJAMIN WACHENJE

www.centralillustration.com

Central Illustration Agency
36 Wellington Street
Covent Garden
London, UK, WC2E 7BD

T: +44(0)20 7240 8925
F: +44(0)20 7836 1177
info@centralillustration.com
www.centralillustration.com

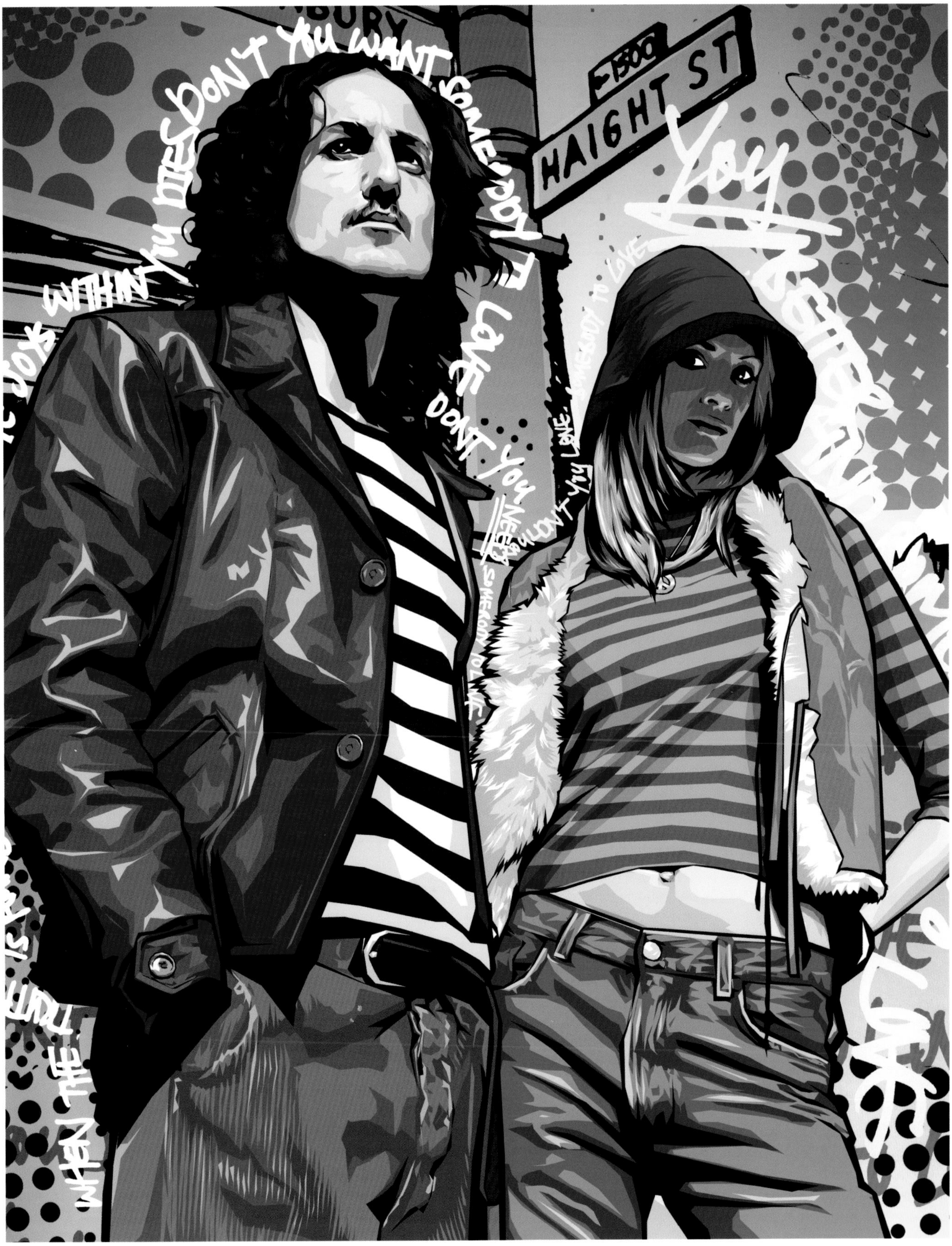

BENJAMIN WACHENJE

Central Illustration Agency
36 Wellington Street
Covent Garden
London, UK, WC2E 7BD

T: +44(0)20 7240 8925
F: +44(0)20 7836 1177
info@centralillustration.com
www.centralillustration.com

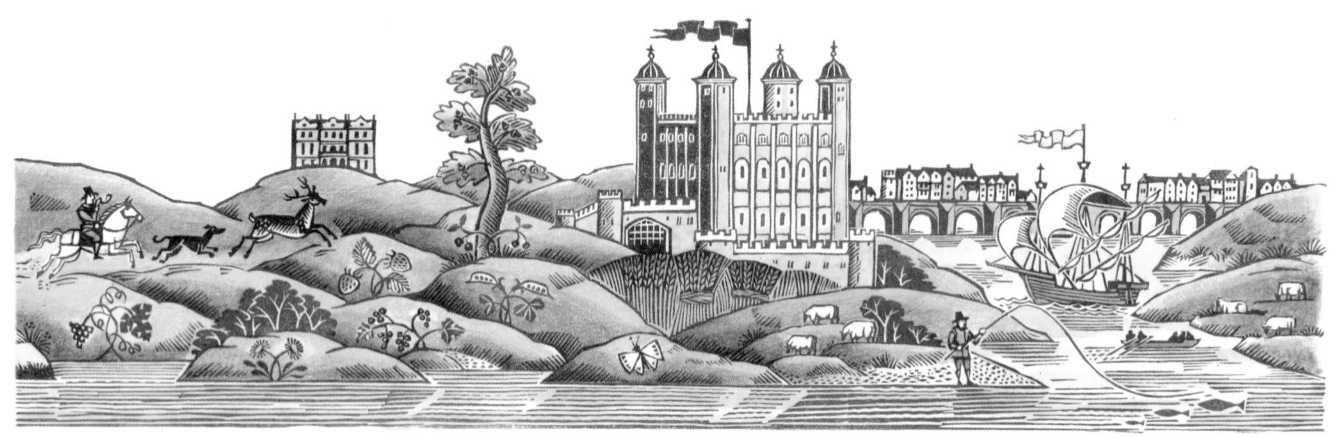

CLARE MELINSKY

www.centralillustration.com

Central Illustration Agency
36 Wellington Street
Covent Garden
London, UK, WC2E 7BD

T: +44(0)20 7240 8925
F: +44(0)20 7836 1177
info@centralillustration.com
www.centralillustration.com

RHS
Chelsea
Flower Show

Tulipa by David Holmes

CHELSEA

RHS FLOWER SHOW 2007

22nd - 26th MAY

Open to members 22nd & 23rd Open to all 24th, 25th & 26th

WWW.RHS.ORG.UK/FLOWERSHOWS

DAVID HOLMES

www.centralillustration.com

Central Illustration Agency
36 Wellington Street
Covent Garden
London, UK, WC2E 7BD

T: +44(0)20 7240 8925
F: +44(0)20 7836 1177
info@centralillustration.com
www.centralillustration.com

BRITISH AIRWAYS

RAY SMITH

Central Illustration Agency
36 Wellington Street
Covent Garden
London, UK, WC2E 7BD

T: +44(0)20 7240 8925
F: +44(0)20 7836 1177
info@centralillustration.com
www.centralillustration.com

RAY SMITH

www.centralillustration.com

Central Illustration Agency
36 Wellington Street
Covent Garden
London, UK, WC2E 7BD

T: +44(0)20 7240 8925
F: +44(0)20 7836 1177
info@centralillustration.com
www.centralillustration.com

JESSIE FORD

Central Illustration Agency
36 Wellington Street
Covent Garden
London, UK, WC2E 7BD

T: +44(0)20 7240 8925
F: +44(0)20 7836 1177
info@centralillustration.com
www.centralillustration.com

NIGEL OWEN

www.centralillustration.com

Central Illustration Agency
36 Wellington Street
Covent Garden
London, UK, WC2E 7BD

T: +44(0)20 7240 8925
F: +44(0)20 7836 1177
info@centralillustration.com
www.centralillustration.com

MAX ELLIS

www.centralillustration.com

Central Illustration Agency
36 Wellington Street
Covent Garden
London, UK, WC2E 7BD

T: +44(0)20 7240 8925
F: +44(0)20 7836 1177
info@centralillustration.com
www.centralillustration.com

Environmentology

MAX ELLIS

www.centralillustration.com

Central Illustration Agency
36 Wellington Street
Covent Garden
London, UK, WC2E 7BD

T: +44(0)20 7240 8925
F: +44(0)20 7836 1177
info@centralillustration.com
www.centralillustration.com

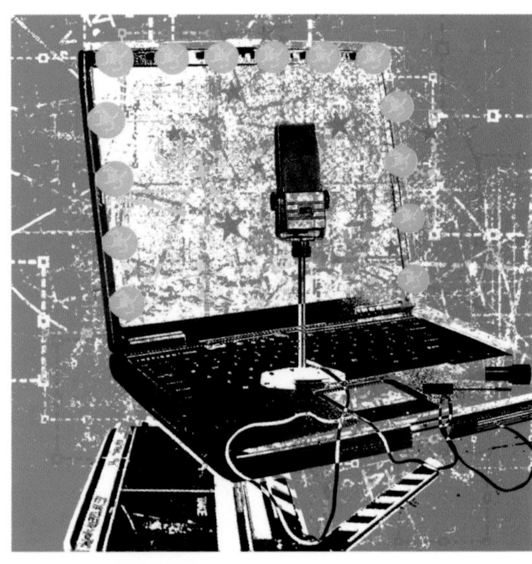

GARY NEILL

Central Illustration Agency
36 Wellington Street
Covent Garden
London, UK, WC2E 7BD

T: +44(0)20 7240 8925
F: +44(0)20 7836 1177
info@centralillustration.com
www.centralillustration.com

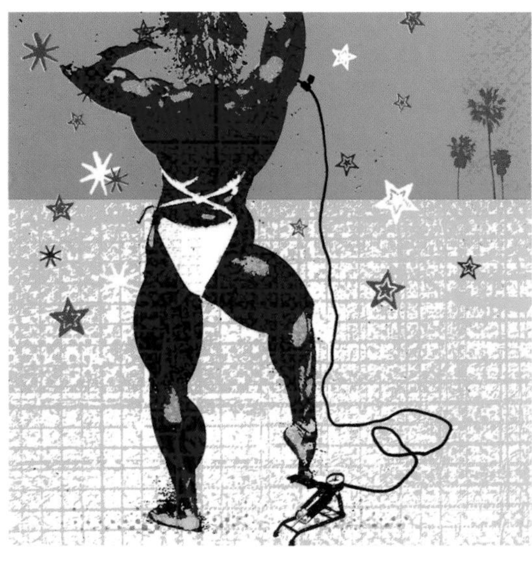

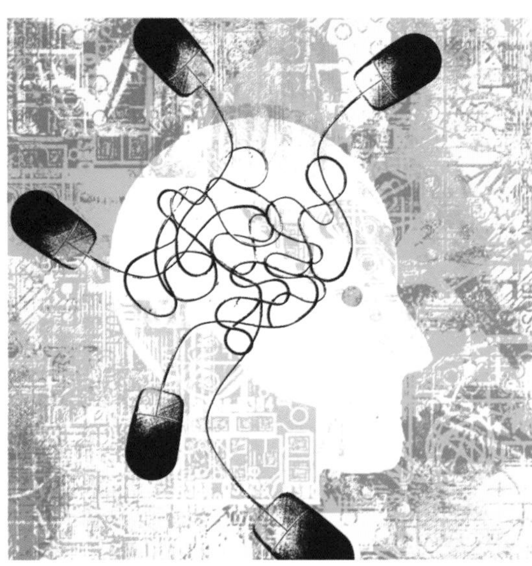

GARY NEILL

www.centralillustration.com

Central Illustration Agency
36 Wellington Street
Covent Garden
London, UK, WC2E 7BD

T: +44(0)20 7240 8925
F: +44(0)20 7836 1177
info@centralillustration.com
www.centralillustration.com

From 'A Prospect of Wales', an essay by Gwyn Jones. First published by Penguin books in 1948.

JOHN SPENCER

Central Illustration Agency
36 Wellington Street
Covent Garden
London, UK, WC2E 7BD

T: +44(0)20 7240 8925
F: +44(0)20 7836 1177
info@centralillustration.com
www.centralillustration.com

THE LANCET Neurology

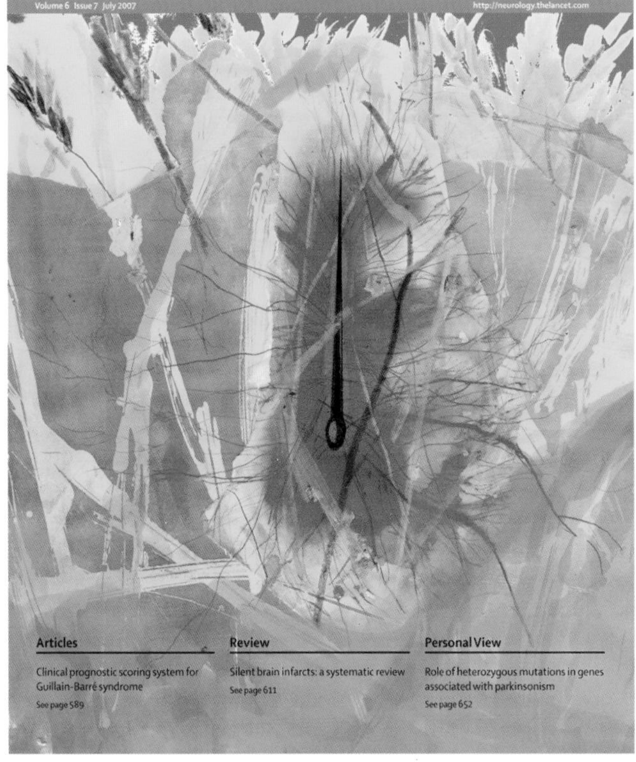

THE LANCET Neurology

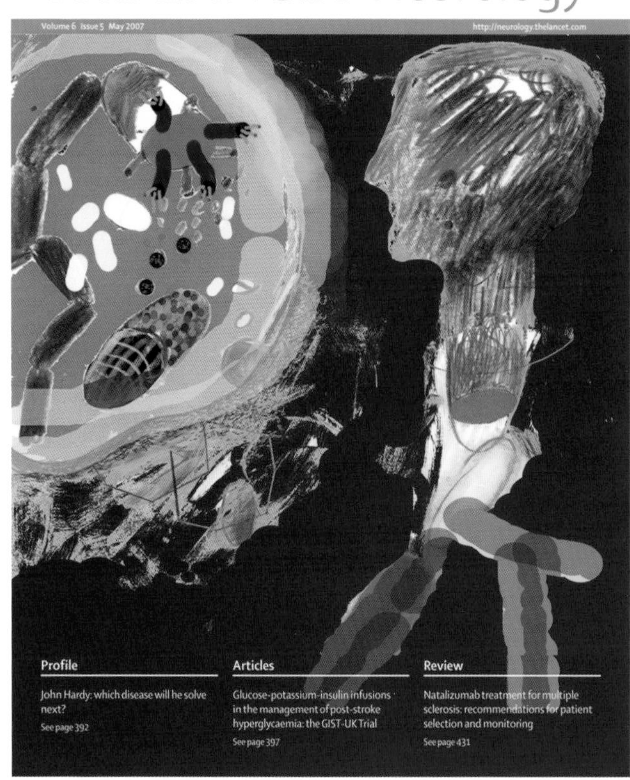

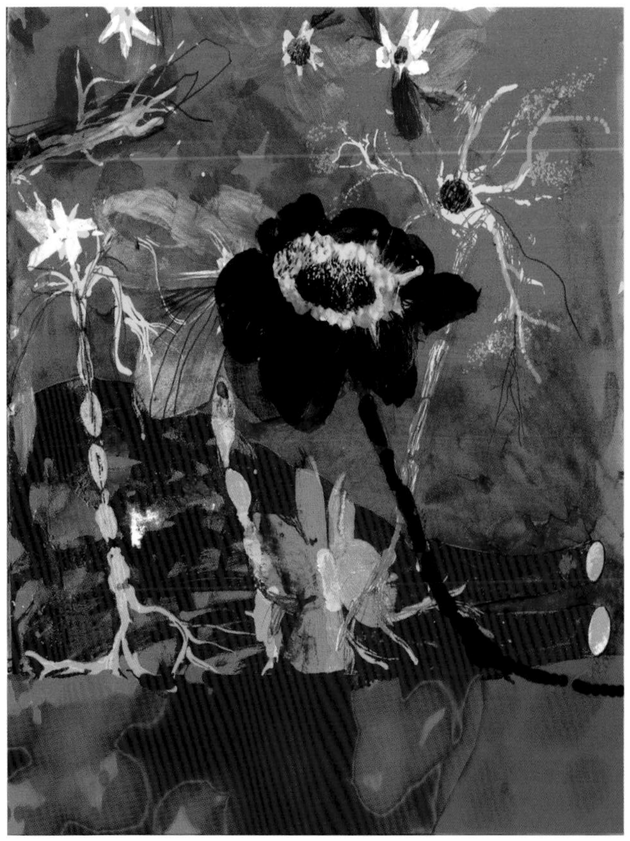

ANDREW FOSTER

www.centralillustration.com

Central Illustration Agency
36 Wellington Street
Covent Garden
London, UK, WC2E 7BD

T: +44(0)20 7240 8925
F: +44(0)20 7836 1177
info@centralillustration.com
www.centralillustration.com

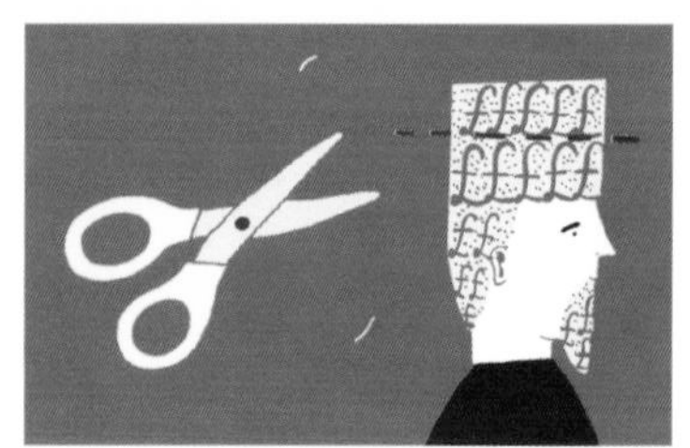

HARRIET RUSSELL

www.centralillustration.com

Central Illustration Agency
36 Wellington Street
Covent Garden
London, UK, WC2E 7BD

T: +44(0)20 7240 8925
F: +44(0)20 7836 1177
info@centralillustration.com
www.centralillustration.com

HARRIET RUSSELL

www.centralillustration.com

Central Illustration Agency
36 Wellington Street
Covent Garden
London, UK, WC2E 7BD

T: +44(0)20 7240 8925
F: +44(0)20 7836 1177
info@centralillustration.com
www.centralillustration.com

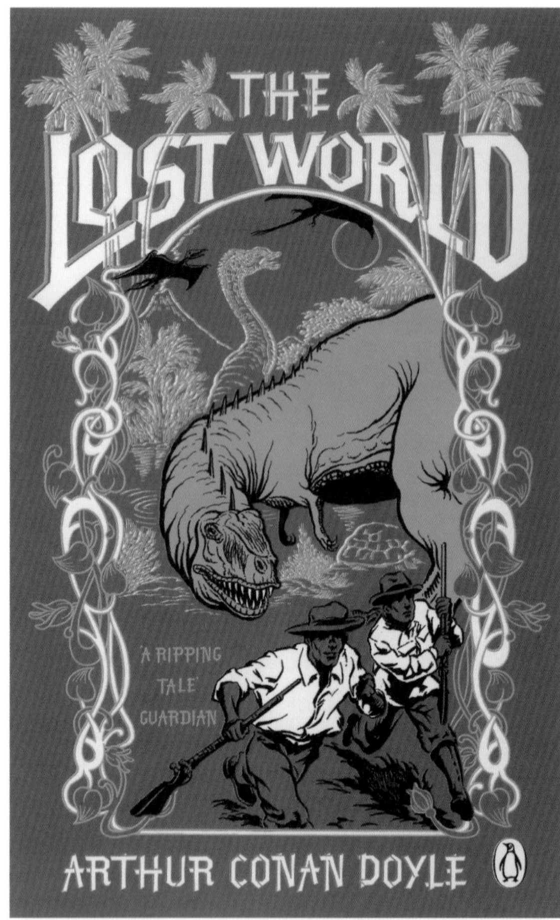

MARK THOMAS

www.centralillustration.com

Central Illustration Agency
36 Wellington Street
Covent Garden
London, UK, WC2E 7BD

T: +44(0)20 7240 8925
F: +44(0)20 7836 1177
info@centralillustration.com
www.centralillustration.com

ANDREW BANNECKER

www.centralillustration.com

Central Illustration Agency
36 Wellington Street
Covent Garden
London, UK, WC2E 7BD

T: +44(0)20 7240 8925
F: +44(0)20 7836 1177
info@centralillustration.com
www.centralillustration.com

JACKIE PARSONS

Central Illustration Agency
36 Wellington Street
Covent Garden
London, UK, WC2E 7BD

T: +44(0)20 7240 8925
F: +44(0)20 7836 1177
info@centralillustration.com
www.centralillustration.com

KATE MILLER

www.centralillustration.com

Central Illustration Agency
36 Wellington Street
Covent Garden
London, UK, WC2E 7BD

T: +44(0)20 7240 8925
F: +44(0)20 7836 1177
info@centralillustration.com
www.centralillustration.com

PAUL OAKLEY

www.centralillustration.com

Central Illustration Agency
36 Wellington Street
Covent Garden
London, UK, WC2E 7BD

T: +44(0)20 7240 8925
F: +44(0)20 7836 1177
info@centralillustration.com
www.centralillustration.com

PAUL OAKLEY

www.centralillustration.com

Central Illustration Agency
36 Wellington Street
Covent Garden
London, UK, WC2E 7BD

T: +44(0)20 7240 8925
F: +44(0)20 7836 1177
info@centralillustration.com
www.centralillustration.com

JONATHAN GIBBS

www.centralillustration.com

Central Illustration Agency
36 Wellington Street
Covent Garden
London, UK, WC2E 7BD

T: +44(0)20 7240 8925
F: +44(0)20 7836 1177
info@centralillustration.com
www.centralillustration.com

TIM MARRS

www.centralillustration.com

Central Illustration Agency
36 Wellington Street
Covent Garden
London, UK, WC2E 7BD

T: +44(0)20 7240 8925
F: +44(0)20 7836 1177
info@centralillustration.com
www.centralillustration.com

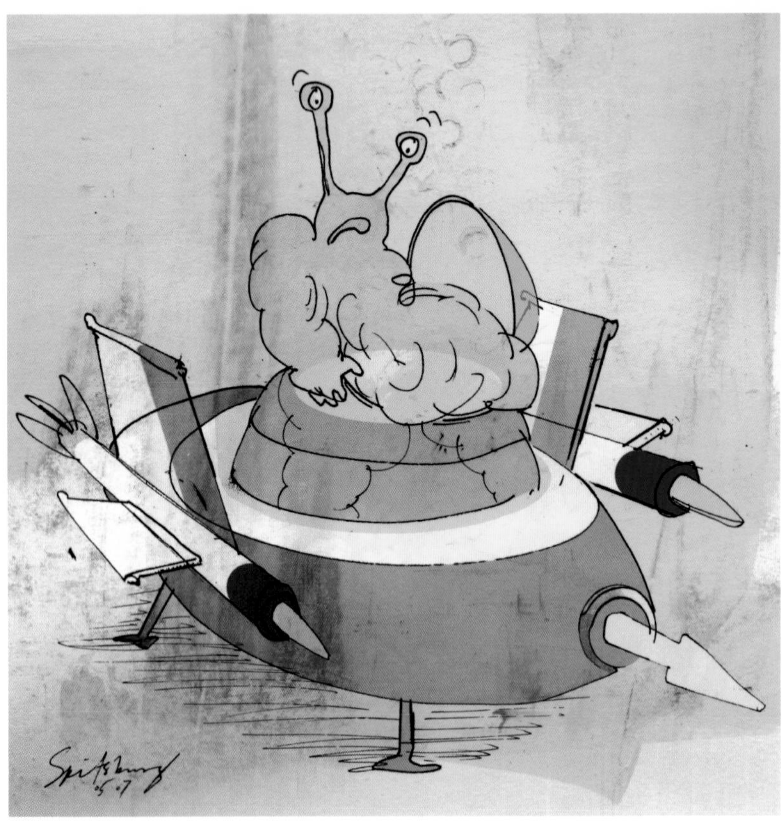

SIMON SPILSBURY

Central Illustration Agency
36 Wellington Street
Covent Garden
London, UK, WC2E 7BD

T: +44(0)20 7240 8925
F: +44(0)20 7836 1177
info@centralillustration.com
www.centralillustration.com

SIMON SPILSBURY

www.centralillustration.com

Central Illustration Agency
36 Wellington Street
Covent Garden
London, UK, WC2E 7BD

T: +44(0)20 7240 8925
F: +44(0)20 7836 1177
info@centralillustration.com
www.centralillustration.com

PAUL WEARING

www.centralillustration.com

Central Illustration Agency
36 Wellington Street
Covent Garden
London, UK, WC2E 7BD

T: +44(0)20 7240 8925
F: +44(0)20 7836 1177
info@centralillustration.com
www.centralillustration.com

PAUL WEARING

www.centralillustration.com

Central Illustration Agency
36 Wellington Street
Covent Garden
London, UK, WC2E 7BD

T: +44(0)20 7240 8925
F: +44(0)20 7836 1177
info@centralillustration.com
www.centralillustration.com

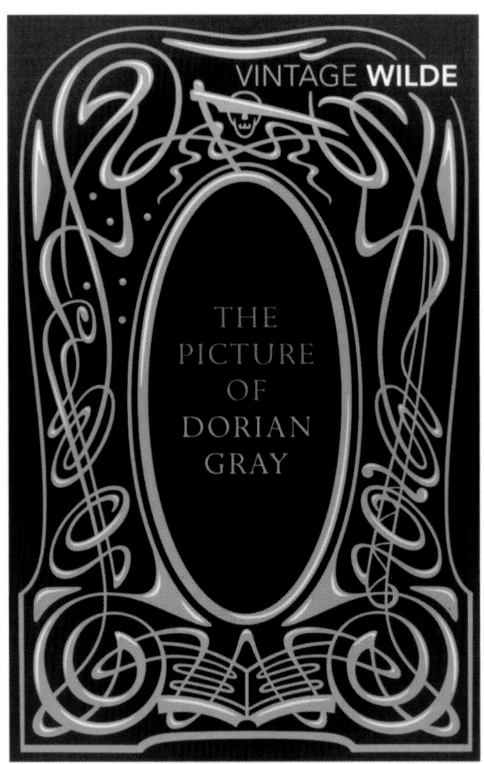

PETER HORRIDGE

www.centralillustration.com

début **art** • Illustrators, Photographers and Fine Artists Agents
30 Tottenham Street, London, W1T 4RJ. United Kingdom
Tel: +44 (0) 20 7636 1064. Fax: +44 (0) 20 7580 7017
The Coningsby Gallery • Tel: +44 (0) 20 7636 7478
email: **info@debutart.com** • **www.debutart.com**

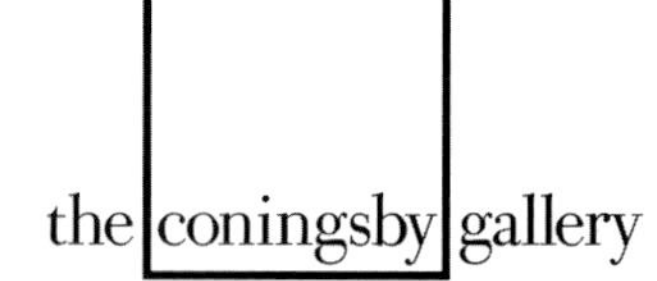

Since 1985, *début* **art** (based in London, England and now with offices in New York, Amsterdam and Sydney) has proactively sought out leading contemporary image-makers & clients who create original, progressive and commercially successful media material. Today, *début* **art** and the highly artistic illustrators it promotes, are widely regarded, both in the UK and around the world, as representing one of the finest and most contemporary talent groupings in the field of illustration.

début **art** and the illustrators it markets have successfully undertaken assignments worldwide for very many companies that are leaders in their fields including: Microsoft, Apple, Coca-Cola, Proctor and Gamble, Samsung, Levi's, Nokia, Rolls-Royce, BP, Shell, Nike, The Chicago Mercantile Exchange, The NYSE, The London Stock Exchange, Citibank, American Express, Barclaycard, HSBC, IBM, British Airways, Unilever, Harrods, Selfridges, Macy's (New York), Verizon, Target, Lucas Inc, The Royal Opera House (London), Universal Music, Sony, Miller, Burton, Harper Collins, The Wall Street Journal, The New York Times, The Times (London), Le Monde, The Economist, The Financial Times, Vogue, Cosmopolitan, Nature and National Geographic Magazine.

Full portfolios for every artist can be reviewed and requested via our web site at **www.debutart.com**

The Coningsby Gallery stages some 30 exhibitions per year by selected leading illustrators, photographers and fine artists. Review of previous exhibitions, a look at upcoming shows and a photo tour of the gallery itself can be accessed at **www.coningsbygallery.com**

Contact: Andrew Coningsby, Samuel Summerskill and Jonathan Hedley.

Joanna Agis
Fusako Akimoto
David Angel
Nicola Antaki
Arno
Tim Ashton
Andrew Baker
Greg Banning
Gary Bates
Glen Baxter
Sara Beazley
Barbara Bellingham
Jon Berkeley
Adrian Bradbury
Norm Breyfogle
Jon Burgerman
Oliver Burston
Benedict Campbell

James Carey
Marina Caruso
Celyn
Container
Sarah Coulston
Matthew Cooper
Peter Crowther
Josie Da-Bank
Matthew Dartford
Carol del Angel
Barry Downard
Elita
Tim Ellis
Flatliner
Flatliner V2
Ewan Fraser
Freya
Peter Grundy

Sarah Hanson
Richard Hart
The Hejz
Matt Herring
Oliver Hibert
Richard Holiday
Nanette Hoogslag
Cathy Horton
Sarah Howell
I Love Dust
Infomen
Jacey
Jaroslav
Sarah Jones
Alan Kitching
Ronald Kurniawan
Christina K
Adam Larson

Neil Leslie
Lie-ins & Tigers
Rob MacDougall
Ric Machin
Daniel Mackie
Harry Malt
Stephane Manel
Gary Marsh
Sophie Marsham
Mauve
Bill McConkey
Kim McGillivray
Vince McIndoe
Claire McMahon
Pat Morgan
Morten Morland
Huntley/Muir
David Newton

Chris Nurse
Sunil Pawar
Ali Pellatt
Pietari Posti
Paul Price
Peter Quinnell
Steve Rawlings
Nick Reddyhoff
Red
Redseal
Kerry Roper
Rouzbeh
Saeko
Serge Seidlitz
Seripop
Craig Shuttlewood
Kid Spaniard
James Starr

Bridget Strachan
Michel Streich
Tado
James Taylor
The Studio
Sophie Toulouse
Dominic Trevett
Alex Trochut
Jim Tsinganos
Vault49
Neil Webb
Webbo
Jane Webster
Louise Weir
Oscar Wilson
Alex Williamson
Tina Zellmer
Jurgen Ziewe

'Beauty is truth, truth beauty'
John Keats

début **art** • Illustrators, Photographers and Fine Artists Agents
30 Tottenham Street, London, W1T 4RJ. United Kingdom
Tel: +44 (0) 20 7636 1064. Fax: +44 (0) 20 7580 7017
The Coningsby Gallery • Tel: +44 (0) 20 7636 7478
email: **info@debutart.com** • **www.debutart.com**

JAMES TAYLOR

début **art** • Illustrators, Photographers and Fine Artists Agents
30 Tottenham Street, London, W1T 4RJ. United Kingdom
Tel: +44 (0) 20 7636 1064. Fax: +44 (0) 20 7580 7017
The Coningsby Gallery • Tel: +44 (0) 20 7636 7478
email: **info@debutart.com** • **www.debutart.com**

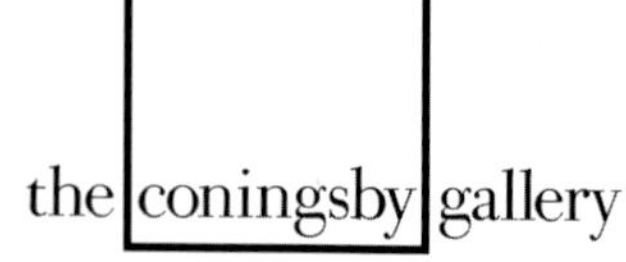

VAULT 49

début **art** • Illustrators, Photographers and Fine Artists Agents
30 Tottenham Street, London, W1T 4RJ. United Kingdom
Tel: +44 (0) 20 7636 1064. Fax: +44 (0) 20 7580 7017
The Coningsby Gallery • Tel: +44 (0) 20 7636 7478
email: **info@debutart.com** • **www.debutart.com**

VAULT 49

www.debutart.com

début **art** • Illustrators, Photographers and Fine Artists Agents
30 Tottenham Street, London, W1T 4RJ. United Kingdom
Tel: +44 (0) 20 7636 1064. Fax: +44 (0) 20 7580 7017
The Coningsby Gallery • Tel: +44 (0) 20 7636 7478
email: **info@debutart.com** • **www.debutart.com**

PATRICK MORGAN

www.debutart.com

début **art** • Illustrators, Photographers and Fine Artists Agents
30 Tottenham Street, London, W1T 4RJ. United Kingdom
Tel: +44 (0) 20 7636 1064. Fax: +44 (0) 20 7580 7017
The Coningsby Gallery • Tel: +44 (0) 20 7636 7478
email: **info@debutart.com** • **www.debutart.com**

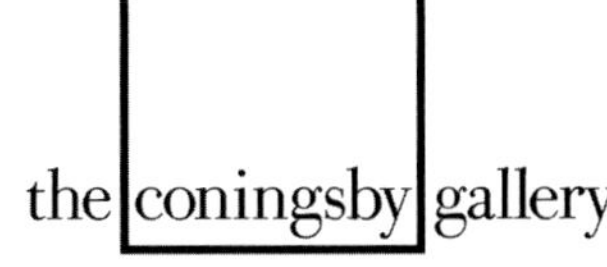

PATRICK MORGAN

www.debutart.com

début **art** • Illustrators, Photographers and Fine Artists Agents
30 Tottenham Street, London, W1T 4RJ. United Kingdom
Tel: +44 (0) 20 7636 1064. Fax: +44 (0) 20 7580 7017
The Coningsby Gallery • Tel: +44 (0) 20 7636 7478
email: **info@debutart.com** • **www.debutart.com**

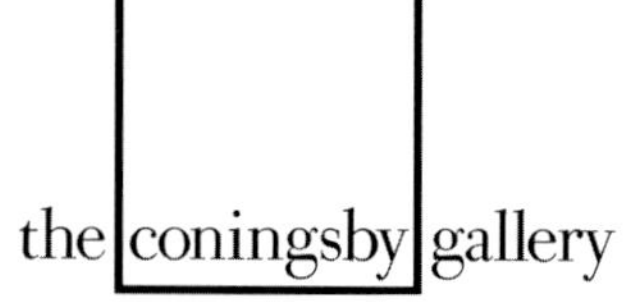

DAVID NEWTON

www.debutart.com

début **art** • Illustrators, Photographers and Fine Artists Agents
30 Tottenham Street, London, W1T 4RJ. United Kingdom
Tel: +44 (0) 20 7636 1064. Fax: +44 (0) 20 7580 7017
The Coningsby Gallery • Tel: +44 (0) 20 7636 7478
email: **info@debutart.com** • **www.debutart.com**

DAVID NEWTON

www.debutart.com

début **art** • Illustrators, Photographers and Fine Artists Agents
30 Tottenham Street, London, W1T 4RJ. United Kingdom
Tel: +44 (0) 20 7636 1064. Fax: +44 (0) 20 7580 7017
The Coningsby Gallery • Tel: +44 (0) 20 7636 7478
email: **info@debutart.com** • **www.debutart.com**

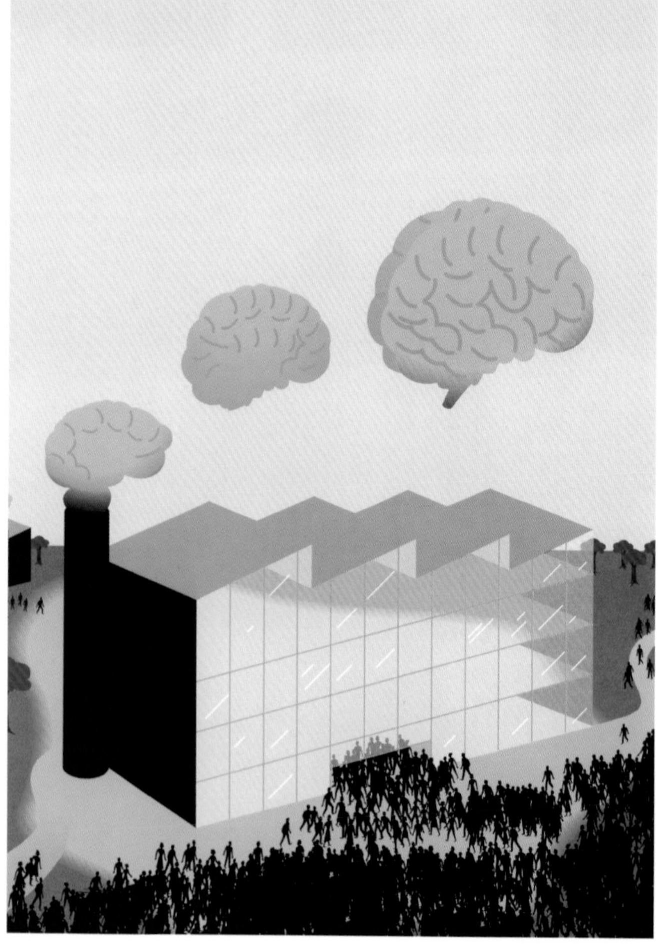

ANDREW BAKER

ANDREW BAKER

www.debutart.com

début **art** • Illustrators, Photographers and Fine Artists Agents
30 Tottenham Street, London, W1T 4RJ. United Kingdom
Tel: +44 (0) 20 7636 1064. Fax: +44 (0) 20 7580 7017
The Coningsby Gallery • Tel: +44 (0) 20 7636 7478
email: **info@debutart.com** • **www.debutart.com**

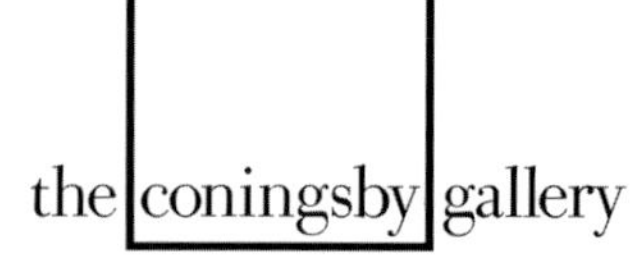

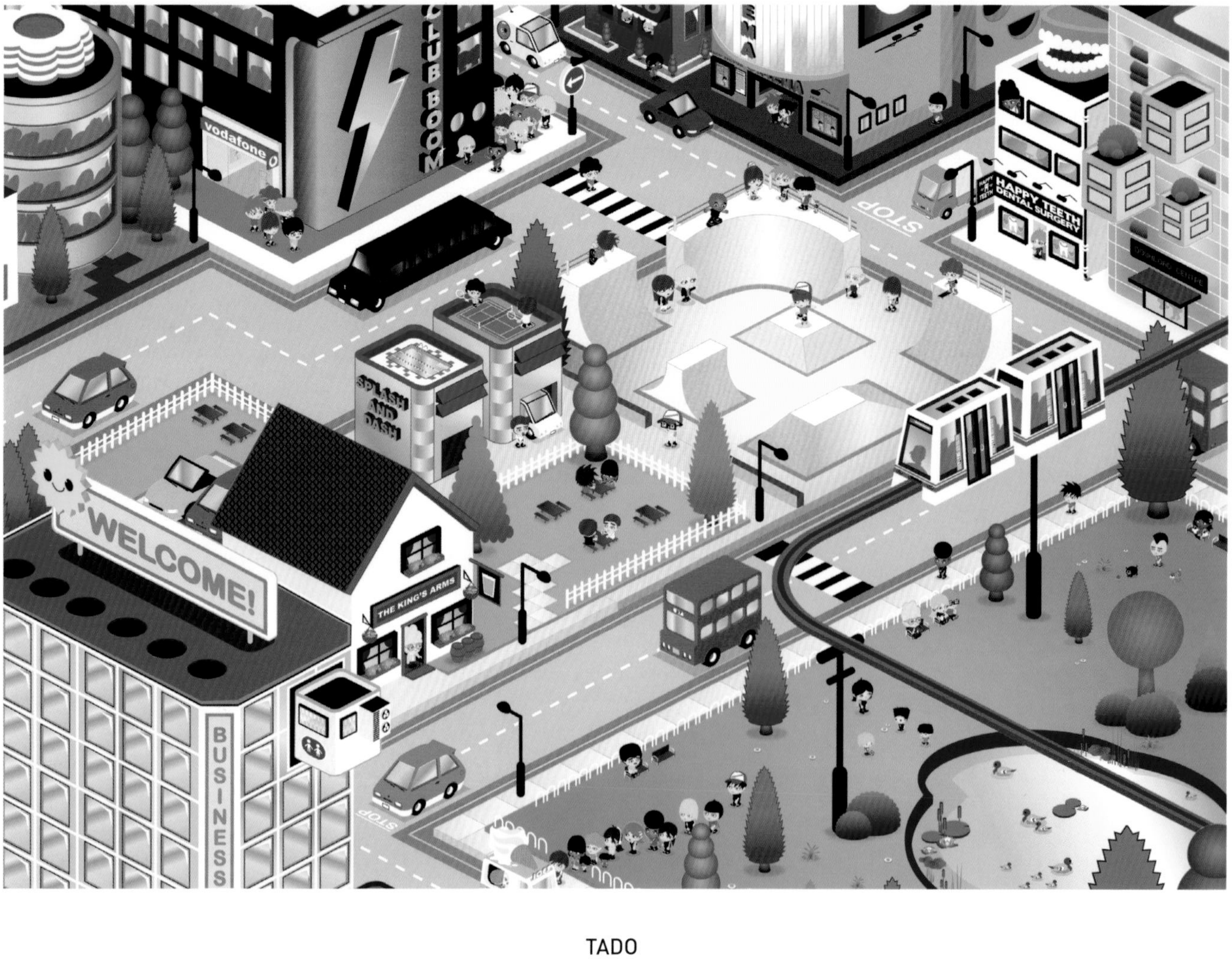

TADO

www.debutart.com

début **art** • Illustrators, Photographers and Fine Artists Agents
30 Tottenham Street, London, W1T 4RJ. United Kingdom
Tel: +44 (0) 20 7636 1064. Fax: +44 (0) 20 7580 7017
The Coningsby Gallery • Tel: +44 (0) 20 7636 7478
email: **info@debutart.com** • **www.debutart.com**

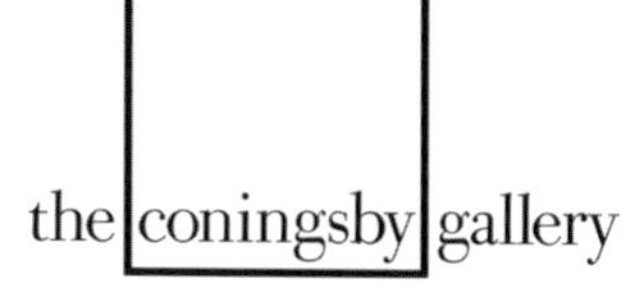

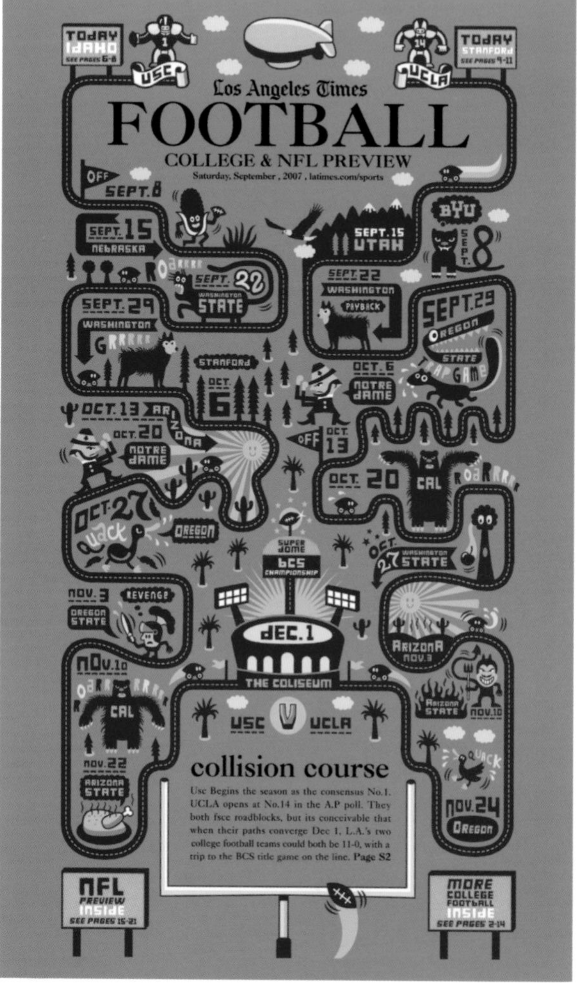

SERGE SEIDLITZ

www.debutart.com

début **art** • Illustrators, Photographers and Fine Artists Agents
30 Tottenham Street, London, W1T 4RJ. United Kingdom
Tel: +44 (0) 20 7636 1064. Fax: +44 (0) 20 7580 7017
The Coningsby Gallery • Tel: +44 (0) 20 7636 7478
email: **info@debutart.com** • **www.debutart.com**

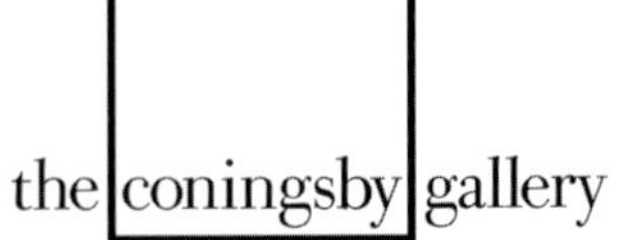

I LOVE DUST

www.debutart.com

début **art** • Illustrators, Photographers and Fine Artists Agents

30 Tottenham Street, London, W1T 4RJ. United Kingdom

Tel: +44 (0) 20 7636 1064. Fax: +44 (0) 20 7580 7017

The Coningsby Gallery • Tel: +44 (0) 20 7636 7478

email: **info@debutart.com** • **www.debutart.com**

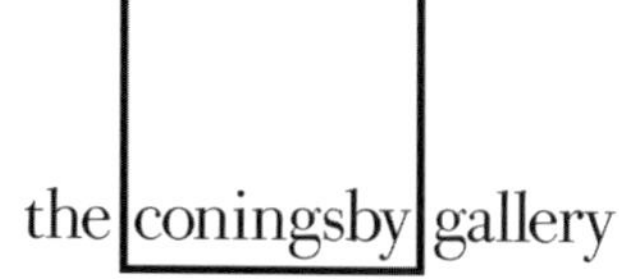

SARAH HOWELL

www.debutart.com

début **art** • Illustrators, Photographers and Fine Artists Agents
30 Tottenham Street, London, W1T 4RJ. United Kingdom
Tel: +44 (0) 20 7636 1064. Fax: +44 (0) 20 7580 7017
The Coningsby Gallery • Tel: +44 (0) 20 7636 7478
email: **info@debutart.com** • **www.debutart.com**

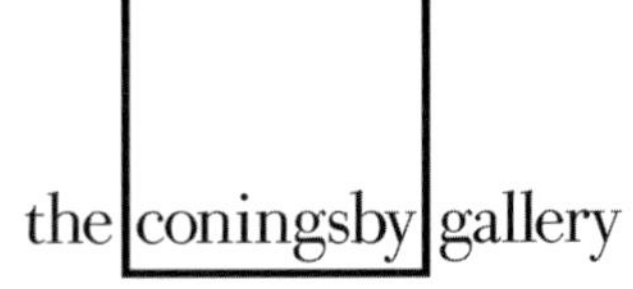

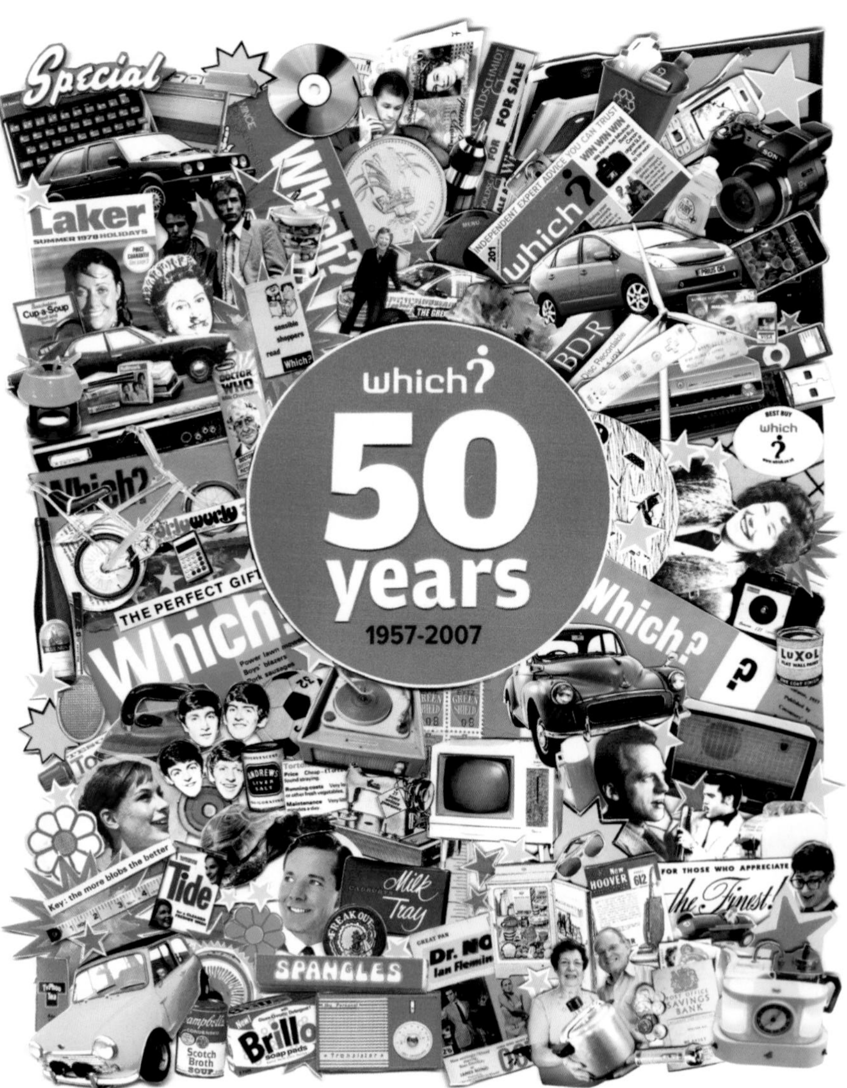

PETER QUINNELL

www.debutart.com

début **art** • Illustrators, Photographers and Fine Artists Agents
30 Tottenham Street, London, W1T 4RJ. United Kingdom
Tel: +44 (0) 20 7636 1064. Fax: +44 (0) 20 7580 7017
The Coningsby Gallery • Tel: +44 (0) 20 7636 7478
email: **info@debutart.com** • **www.debutart.com**

JON BURGERMAN

www.debutart.com

début **art** • Illustrators, Photographers and Fine Artists Agents
30 Tottenham Street, London, W1T 4RJ. United Kingdom
Tel: +44 (0) 20 7636 1064. Fax: +44 (0) 20 7580 7017
The Coningsby Gallery • Tel: +44 (0) 20 7636 7478
email: **info@debutart.com** • **www.debutart.com**

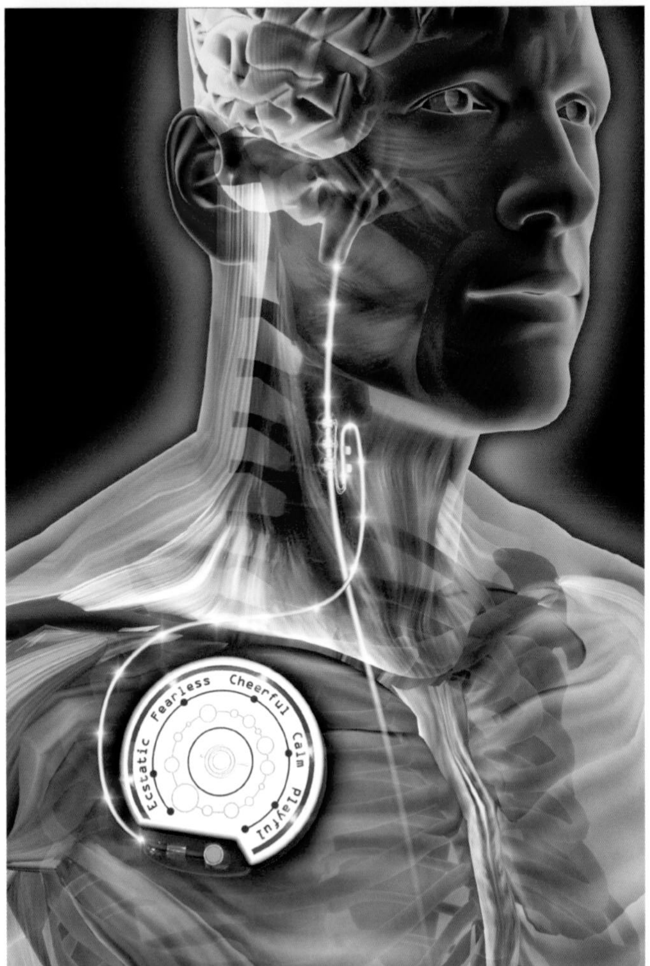

OLIVER BURSTON

www.debutart.com

début **art** • Illustrators, Photographers and Fine Artists Agents
30 Tottenham Street, London, W1T 4RJ. United Kingdom
Tel: +44 (0) 20 7636 1064. Fax: +44 (0) 20 7580 7017
The Coningsby Gallery • Tel: +44 (0) 20 7636 7478
email: **info@debutart.com** • **www.debutart.com**

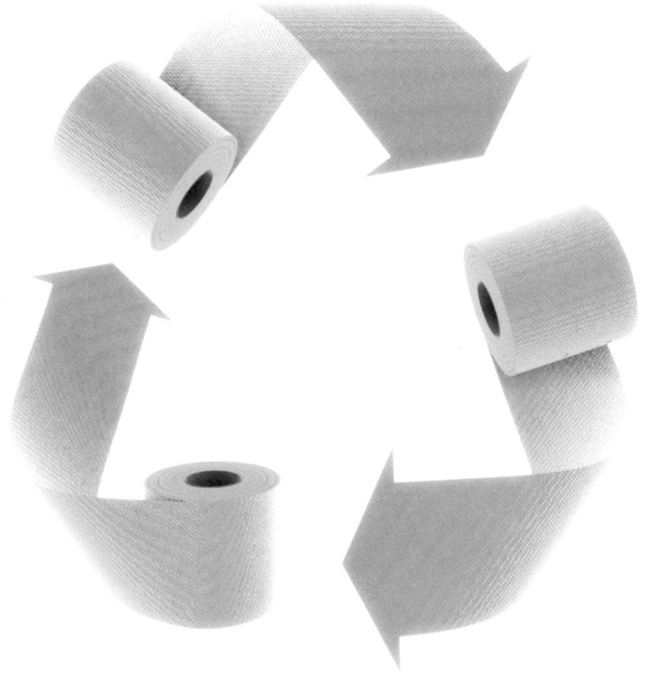

PETER CROWTHER

www.debutart.com

début **art** • Illustrators, Photographers and Fine Artists Agents
30 Tottenham Street, London, W1T 4RJ. United Kingdom
Tel: +44 (0) 20 7636 1064. Fax: +44 (0) 20 7580 7017
The Coningsby Gallery • Tel: +44 (0) 20 7636 7478
email: **info@debutart.com** • **www.debutart.com**

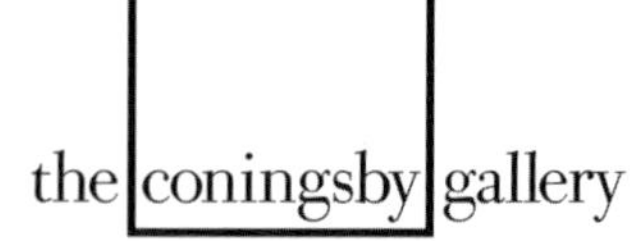

MARINA CARUSO

www.debutart.com

début **art** • Illustrators, Photographers and Fine Artists Agents
30 Tottenham Street, London, W1T 4RJ. United Kingdom
Tel: +44 (0) 20 7636 1064. Fax: +44 (0) 20 7580 7017
The Coningsby Gallery • Tel: +44 (0) 20 7636 7478
email: **info@debutart.com** • **www.debutart.com**

ALEX WILLIAMSON

www.debutart.com

début **art** • Illustrators, Photographers and Fine Artists Agents
30 Tottenham Street, London, W1T 4RJ. United Kingdom
Tel: +44 (0) 20 7636 1064. Fax: +44 (0) 20 7580 7017
The Coningsby Gallery • Tel: +44 (0) 20 7636 7478
email: **info@debutart.com** • **www.debutart.com**

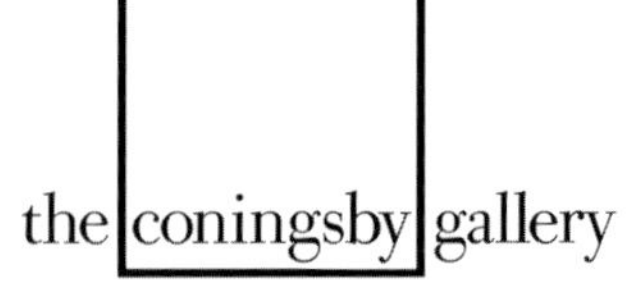

KERRY ROPER

www.debutart.com

début **art** • Illustrators, Photographers and Fine Artists Agents
30 Tottenham Street, London, W1T 4RJ. United Kingdom
Tel: +44 (0) 20 7636 1064. Fax: +44 (0) 20 7580 7017
The Coningsby Gallery • Tel: +44 (0) 20 7636 7478
email: **info@debutart.com** • **www.debutart.com**

JAMES CAREY

www.debutart.com

début **art** • Illustrators, Photographers and Fine Artists Agents
30 Tottenham Street, London, W1T 4RJ. United Kingdom
Tel: +44 (0) 20 7636 1064. Fax: +44 (0) 20 7580 7017
The Coningsby Gallery • Tel: +44 (0) 20 7636 7478
email: **info@debutart.com** • **www.debutart.com**

the coningsby gallery

NEIL WEBB

www.debutart.com

début **art** • Illustrators, Photographers and Fine Artists Agents
30 Tottenham Street, London, W1T 4RJ. United Kingdom
Tel: +44 (0) 20 7636 1064. Fax: +44 (0) 20 7580 7017
The Coningsby Gallery • Tel: +44 (0) 20 7636 7478
email: **info@debutart.com** • **www.debutart.com**

TIM ELLIS

www.debutart.com

début **art** • Illustrators, Photographers and Fine Artists Agents
30 Tottenham Street, London, W1T 4RJ. United Kingdom
Tel: +44 (0) 20 7636 1064. Fax: +44 (0) 20 7580 7017
The Coningsby Gallery • Tel: +44 (0) 20 7636 7478
email: **info@debutart.com** • **www.debutart.com**

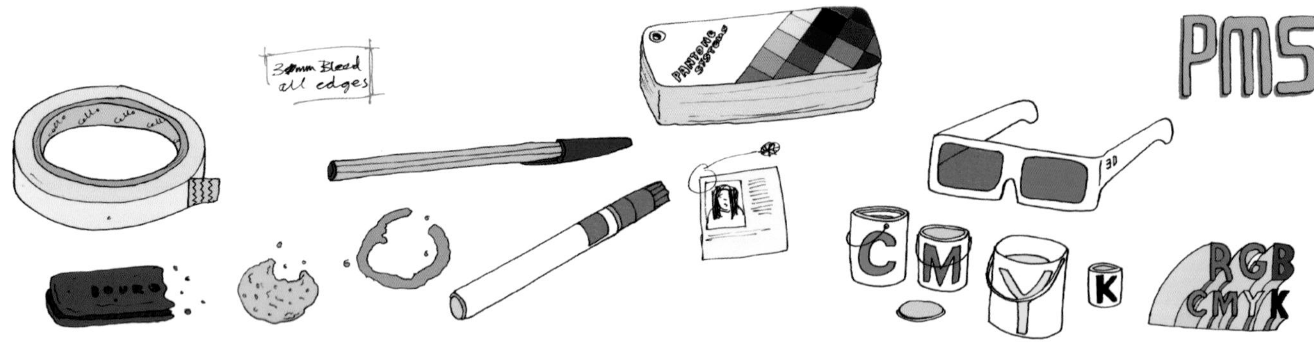

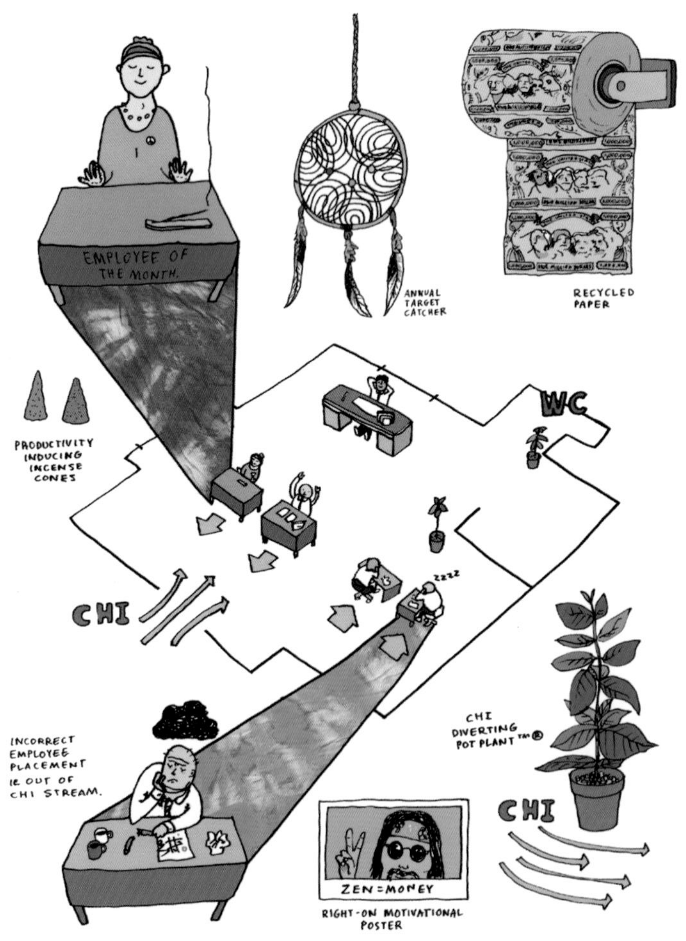

HARRY MALT

www.debutart.com

début **art** • Illustrators, Photographers and Fine Artists Agents
30 Tottenham Street, London, W1T 4RJ. United Kingdom
Tel: +44 (0) 20 7636 1064. Fax: +44 (0) 20 7580 7017
The Coningsby Gallery • Tel: +44 (0) 20 7636 7478
email: **info@debutart.com** • **www.debutart.com**

MATTHEW DARTFORD

www.debutart.com

début **art** • Illustrators, Photographers and Fine Artists Agents
30 Tottenham Street, London, W1T 4RJ. United Kingdom
Tel: +44 (0) 20 7636 1064. Fax: +44 (0) 20 7580 7017
The Coningsby Gallery • Tel: +44 (0) 20 7636 7478
email: **info@debutart.com** • **www.debutart.com**

JACKDAW

www.debutart.com

début **art** • Illustrators, Photographers and Fine Artists Agents
30 Tottenham Street, London, W1T 4RJ. United Kingdom
Tel: +44 (0) 20 7636 1064. Fax: +44 (0) 20 7580 7017
The Coningsby Gallery • Tel: +44 (0) 20 7636 7478
email: **info@debutart.com** • **www.debutart.com**

FLATLINER V2

www.debutart.com

début **art** • Illustrators, Photographers and Fine Artists Agents
30 Tottenham Street, London, W1T 4RJ. United Kingdom
Tel: +44 (0) 20 7636 1064. Fax: +44 (0) 20 7580 7017
The Coningsby Gallery • Tel: +44 (0) 20 7636 7478
email: **info@debutart.com** • **www.debutart.com**

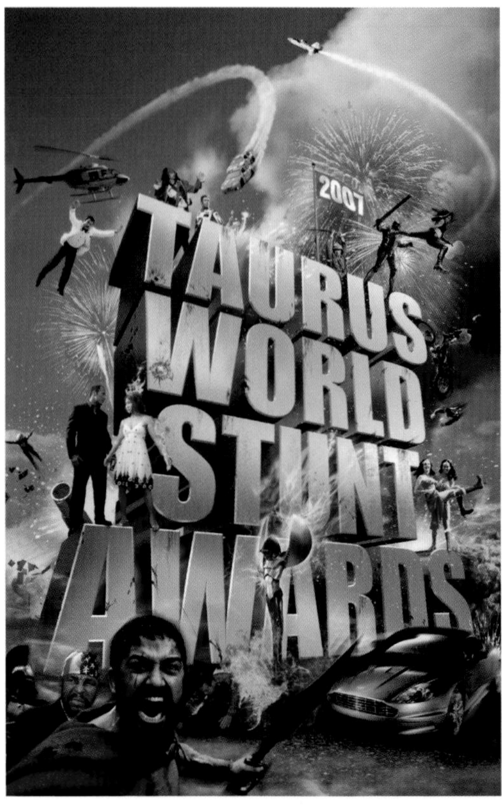

JEFF WACK

www.debutart.com

www.folioart.co.uk
10 Gate Street, Lincoln's Inn Fields, London, WC2A 3HP
E. all@folioart.co.uk | T. +44 (0)20 7242 9562 | F. +44 (0)20 7242 1816

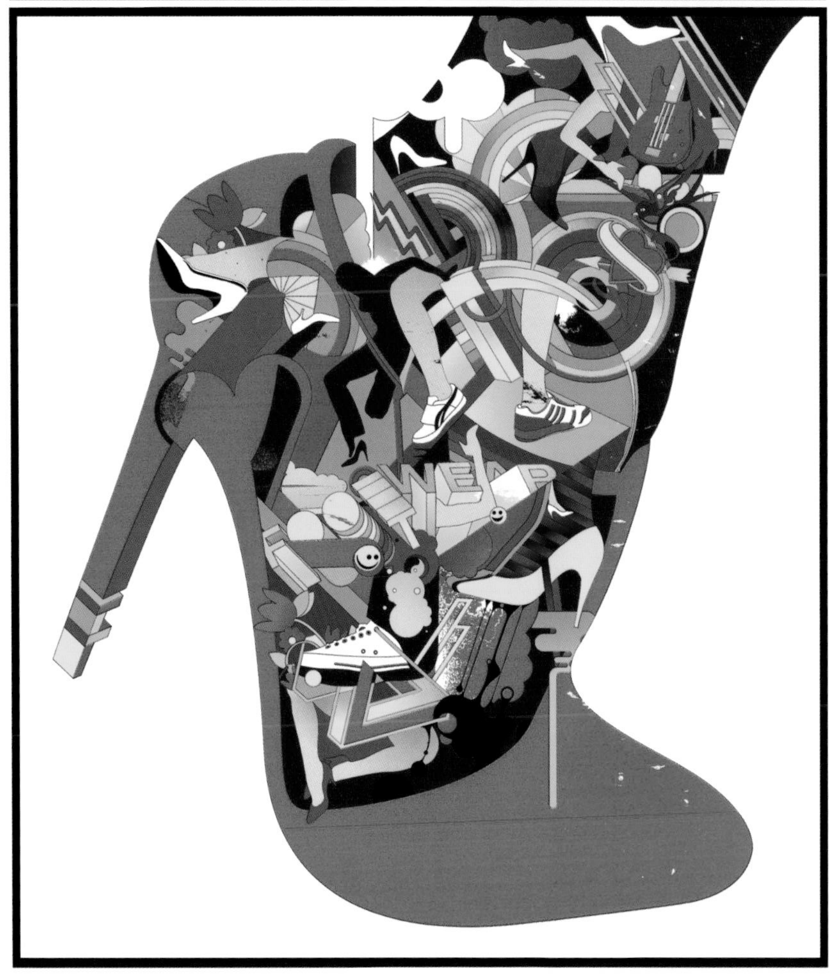

JAMIE CULLEN

www.folioart.co.uk

www.folioart.co.uk

10 Gate Street, Lincoln's Inn Fields, London, WC2A 3HP
E. all@folioart.co.uk | T. +44 (0)20 7242 9562 | F. +44 (0)20 7242 1816

JASON BROOKS

www.folioart.co.uk

www.folioart.co.uk
10 Gate Street, Lincoln's Inn Fields, London, WC2A 3HP
E. all@folioart.co.uk | T. +44 (0)20 7242 9562 | F. +44 (0)20 7242 1816

JASON BROOKS

www.folioart.co.uk

10 Gate Street, Lincoln's Inn Fields, London, WC2A 3HP
E. all@folioart.co.uk | T. +44 (0)20 7242 9562 | F. +44 (0)20 7242 1816

TOBY LEIGH

www.folioart.co.uk

10 Gate Street, Lincoln's Inn Fields, London, WC2A 3HP

E. all@folioart.co.uk | T. +44 (0)20 7242 9562 | F. +44 (0)20 7242 1816

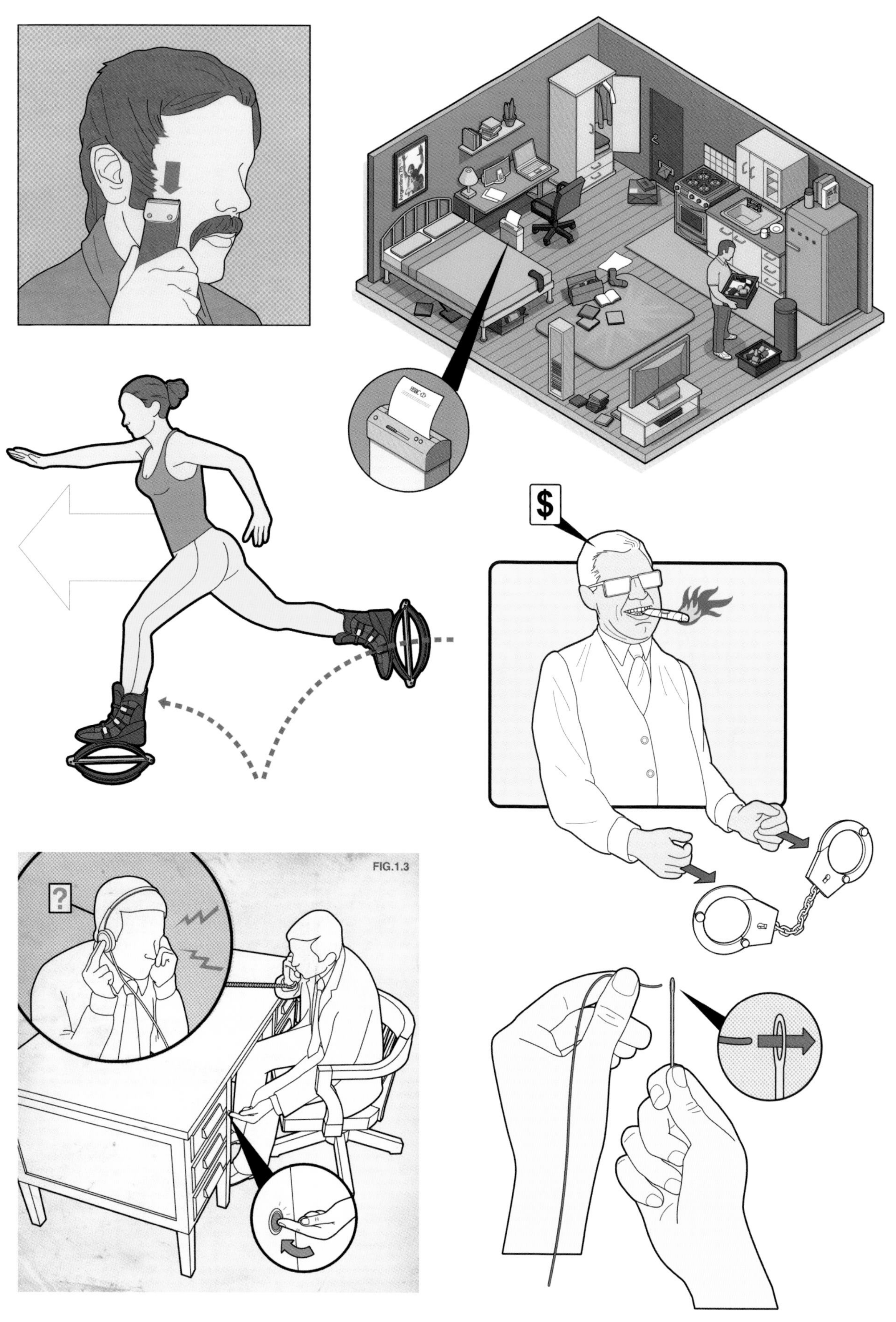

TOBATRON

www.folioart.co.uk

www.folioart.co.uk
10 Gate Street, Lincoln's Inn Fields, London, WC2A 3HP
E. all@folioart.co.uk | T. +44 (0)20 7242 9562 | F. +44 (0)20 7242 1816

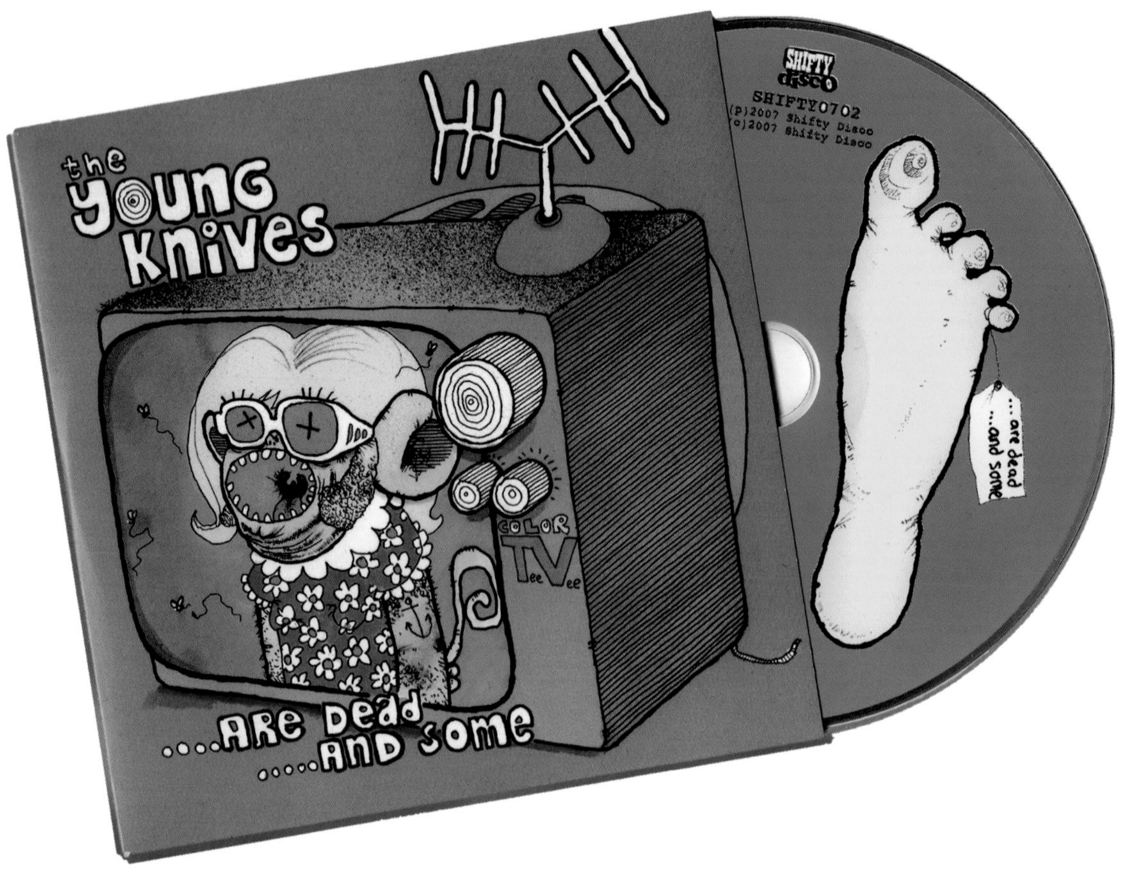

ANDY WATT

www.folioart.co.uk
10 Gate Street, Lincoln's Inn Fields, London, WC2A 3HP
E. all@folioart.co.uk | T. +44 (0)20 7242 9562 | F. +44 (0)20 7242 1816

DAVID JUNIPER

www.folioart.co.uk

www.folioart.co.uk
10 Gate Street, Lincoln's Inn Fields, London, WC2A 3HP
E. all@folioart.co.uk | T. +44 (0)20 7242 9562 | F. +44 (0)20 7242 1816

LISA EVANS

LISA EVANS

www.folioart.co.uk

www.folioart.co.uk

10 Gate Street, Lincoln's Inn Fields, London, WC2A 3HP
E. all@folioart.co.uk | T. +44 (0)20 7242 9562 | F. +44 (0)20 7242 1816

You are invited to a week of gorgeousness

VERONICA PALMIERI

www.folioart.co.uk

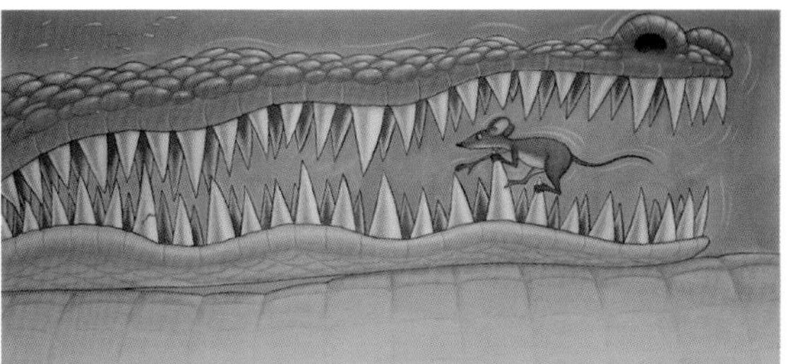

MIKE TERRY

www.folioart.co.uk

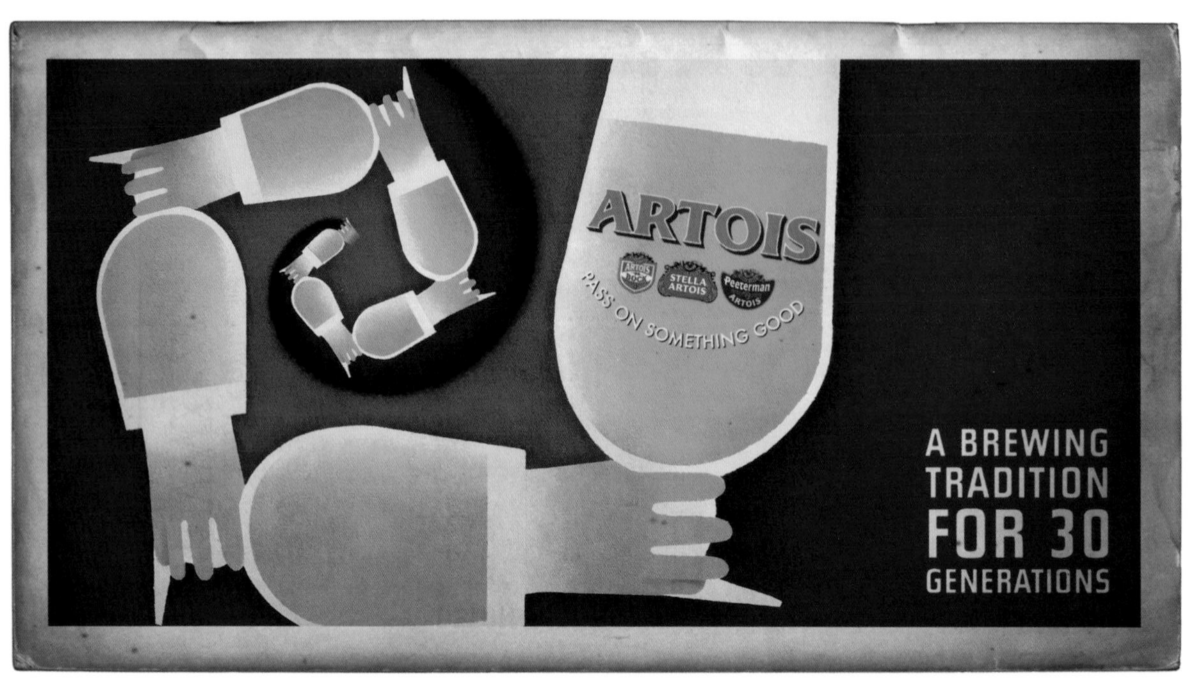

DAVID LAWRENCE

www.folioart.co.uk

www.folioart.co.uk
10 Gate Street, Lincoln's Inn Fields, London, WC2A 3HP
E. all@folioart.co.uk | T. +44 (0)20 7242 9562 | F. +44 (0)20 7242 1816

DAVID LAWRENCE

www.folioart.co.uk

www.folioart.co.uk

10 Gate Street, Lincoln's Inn Fields, London, WC2A 3HP

E. all@folioart.co.uk | T. +44 (0)20 7242 9562 | F. +44 (0)20 7242 1816

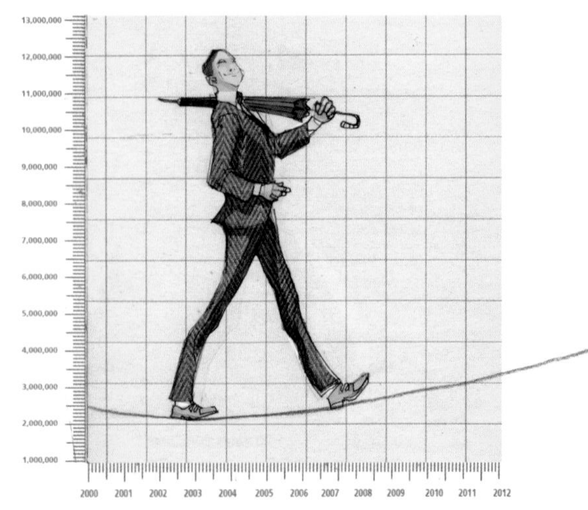

ALEX GREEN

www.folioart.co.uk

www.folioart.co.uk
10 Gate Street, Lincoln's Inn Fields, London, WC2A 3HP
E. all@folioart.co.uk | T. +44 (0)20 7242 9562 | F. +44 (0)20 7242 1816

RUI RICARDO

www.folioart.co.uk

10 Gate Street, Lincoln's Inn Fields, London, WC2A 3HP
E. all@folioart.co.uk | T. +44 (0)20 7242 9562 | F. +44 (0)20 7242 1816

MISS SWANNE

JOSIE JO

BRITTA STENHOUSE

JAMIE JAY

10 Gate Street, Lincoln's Inn Fields, London, WC2A 3HP
E. all@folioart.co.uk | T. +44 (0)20 7242 9562 | F. +44 (0)20 7242 1816

ED MCLACHLAN

MARIA COLINO

CATALINA ESTRADA

10 Gate Street, Lincoln's Inn Fields, London, WC2A 3HP
E. all@folioart.co.uk | T. +44 (0)20 7242 9562 | F. +44 (0)20 7242 1816

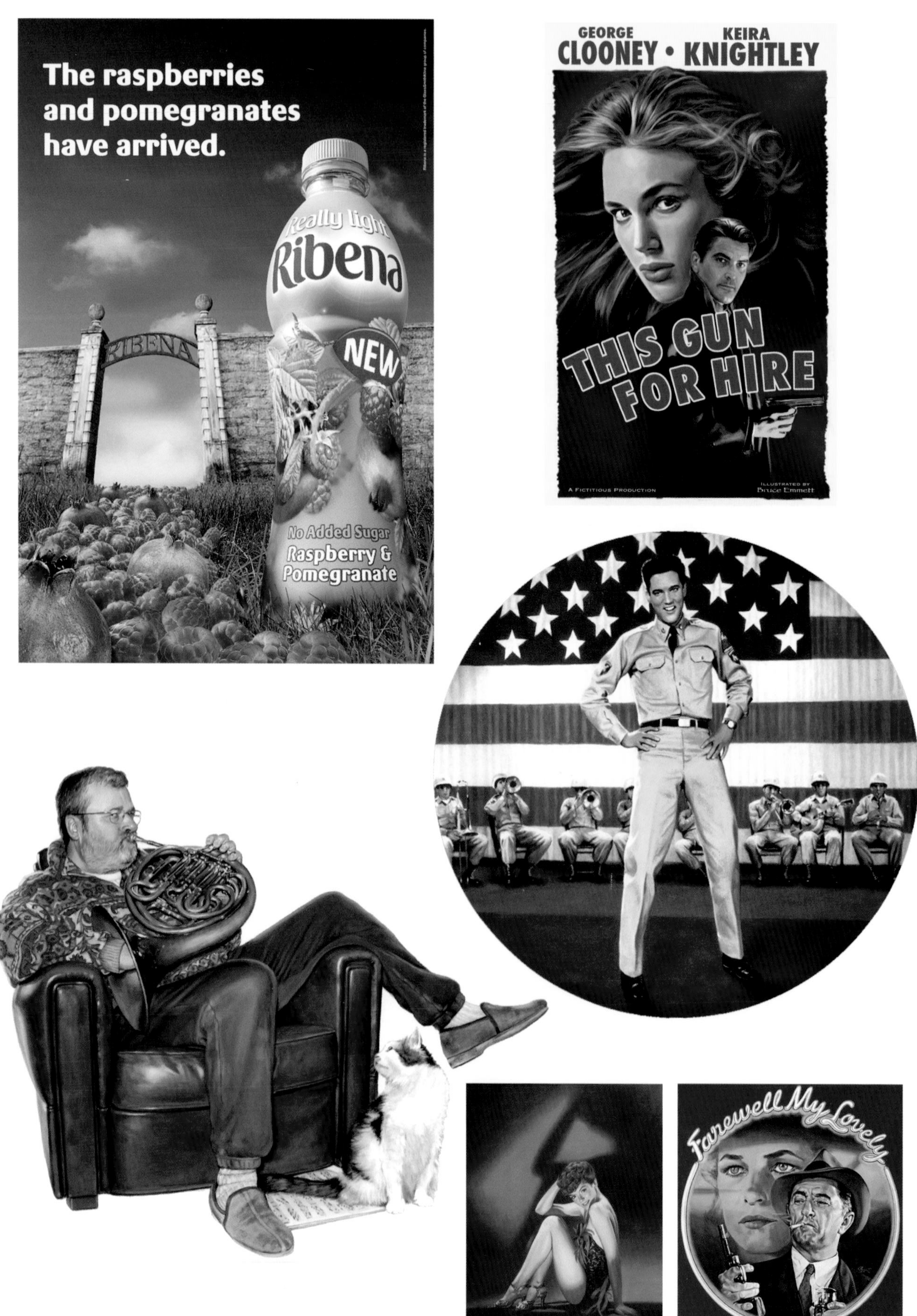

BRUCE EMMETT

www.folioart.co.uk
10 Gate Street, Lincoln's Inn Fields, London, WC2A 3HP
E. all@folioart.co.uk | T. +44 (0)20 7242 9562 | F. +44 (0)20 7242 1816

SYD BRAK

ANNE SHARP

www.folioart.co.uk
10 Gate Street, Lincoln's Inn Fields, London, WC2A 3HP
E. all@folioart.co.uk | T. +44 (0)20 7242 9562 | F. +44 (0)20 7242 1816

ROGER WATT

BRENDAN KELLY

JILL BARTHORPE

www.folioart.co.uk
10 Gate Street, Lincoln's Inn Fields, London, WC2A 3HP
E. all@folioart.co.uk | T. +44 (0)20 7242 9562 | F. +44 (0)20 7242 1816

JULIAN DE NARVAEZ

www.folioart.co.uk

Folio Boutique

Limited-edition prints in association with the Folio agency

www.folioboutique.com

Gez Fry — Hot Version

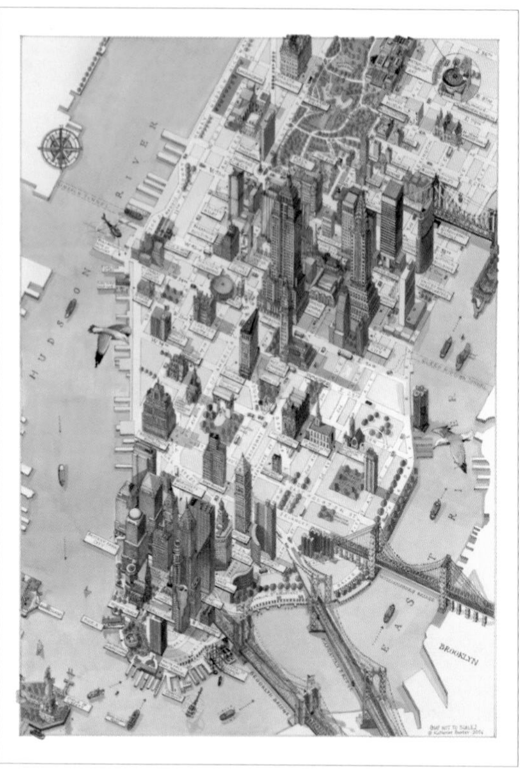

Katherine Baxter — New York

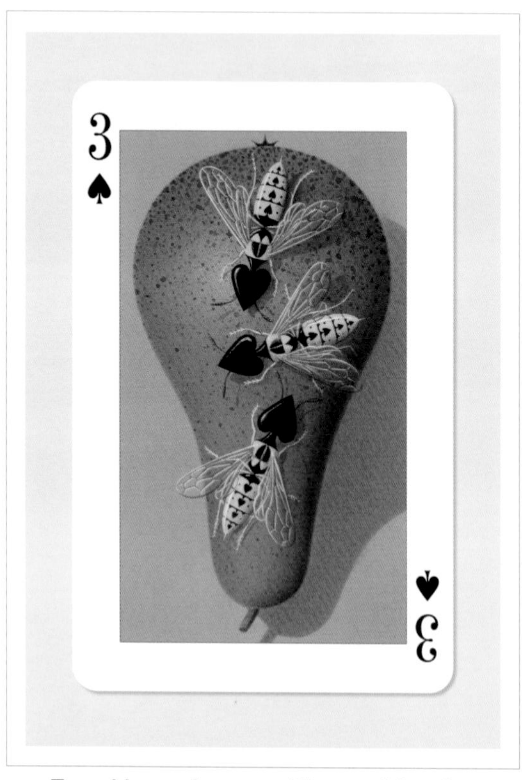

Tony Meeuwissen — Three of Spades

Syd Brak — Wired for Sound

JO BIRD JOSEPH BLAKEY FABIO CORUZZI KAREN CHEUNG INGI ERLINGSSON MARILINE FIORI KATE FORRESTER
CHRISTOPHER HADJINICOLA MATT JOHNSTONE JOHNNY MAC SIM MARRIOT MIGY DAN MUMFORD
RALPH MAUGARITE SAUVAGE JEM ROBINSON CAROLINE TOMLINSON DAMIEN WEIGHILL NED WOODMAN
SIMON ALLAN ELLIOTT CLIFFORD BRIGGS CHRIS COOPER NEIL GITTINS ILOVEDUST KINETIC MESH MATT LATCHFORD
MINA SONG EWEN STENHOUSE PETER TAYLOR YAW ADAM VRIJLAND TRISTAN WICKHAM JELLY MOTION

RALPH

SIM MARRIOT

jelly

illustration
motion graphics
animation
creative solutions

MARILINE FIORI

MARGUERITE SAUVAGE

www.jellylondon.com

9-10 charlotte mews, london w1t 4ef
t: 020 7323 3307 f: 020 7636 2455
www.jellylondon.com

JO BIRD

KATE FORRESTER

jelly

illustration
motion graphics
animation
creative solutions

DAN MUMFORD

DAMIEN WEIGHILL

www.jellylondon.com

9-10 charlotte mews, london w1t 4ef
t: 020 7323 3307 f: 020 7636 2455
www.jellylondon.com

NED WOODMAN

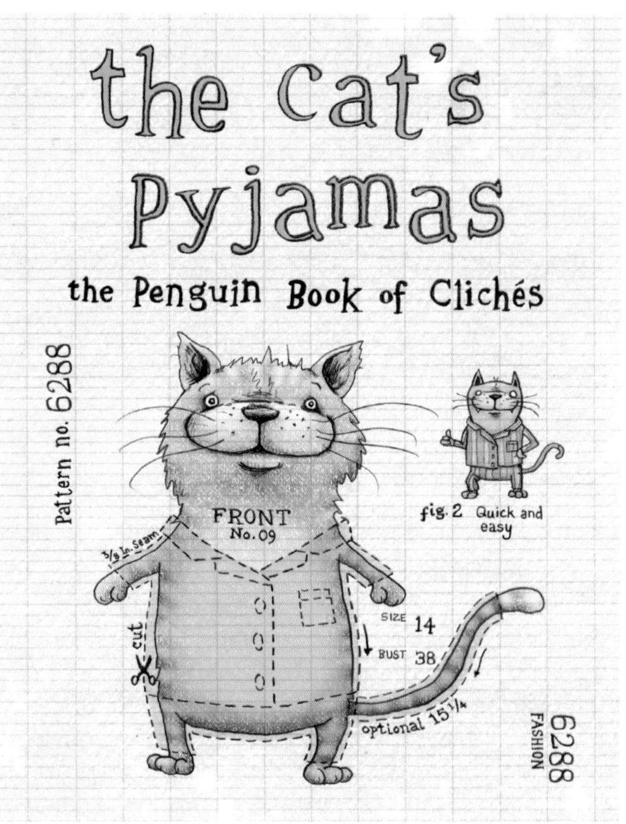

KAREN CHEUNG

JEM ROBINSON

MATT JOHNSTONE

www.jellylondon.com

9-10 charlotte mews, london w1t 4ef
t: 020 7323 3307 f: 020 7636 2455
www.jellylondon.com

JOSEPH BLAKEY

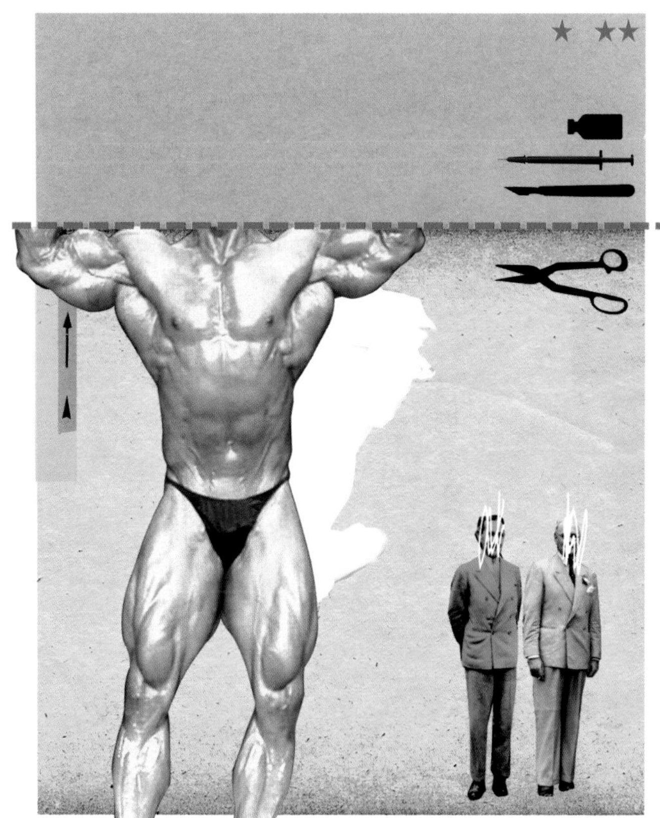

CAROLINE TOMLINSON

illustration
motion graphics
animation
creative solutions

9-10 charlotte mews, london w1t 4ef
t: 020 7323 3307 f: 020 7636 2455
www.jellylondon.com

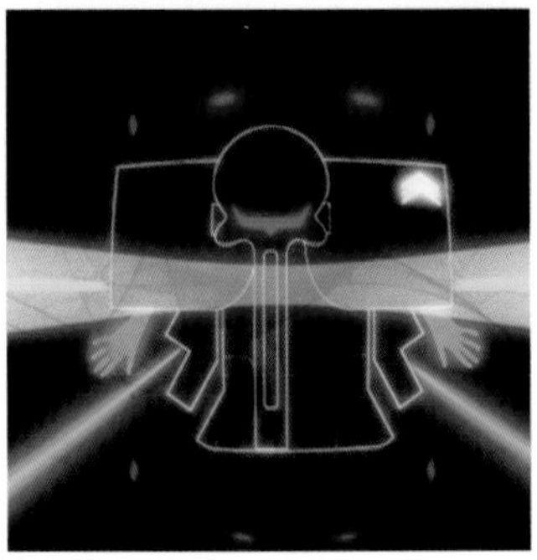

JELLY MOTION

www.jellylondon.com

LEMONADE

ILLUSTRATION AGENCY // **VOICE :** 07891 390750 // **EMAIL :** INFO@LEMONADEILLUSTRATION.COM
WEB : LEMONADEILLUSTRATION.COM // **OFFICE :** HILL HOUSE, SUITE 231, 210 UPPER RICHMOND RD, LONDON //

We are fast expanding our services to the creative industry as illustration increases in popularity and the lines blur as to what media illustrators use to get their ideas across.

Please go online to see the three **new** sections to our site and view the full extent of our portfolio of artists specialising in all media from print to animation

LEMONADE MOTION //

LEMONADE STORYBOARDS //

LEMONADE CORPORATE IDENTITY //

LEMONADE

ILLUSTRATION AGENCY // **VOICE :** 07891 390750 // **EMAIL :** INFO@LEMONADEILLUSTRATION.COM
WEB : LEMONADEILLUSTRATION.COM // **OFFICE :** HILL HOUSE, SUITE 231, 210 UPPER RICHMOND RD, LONDON //

LEMONADE STORYBOARDS

www.lemonadeillustration.com

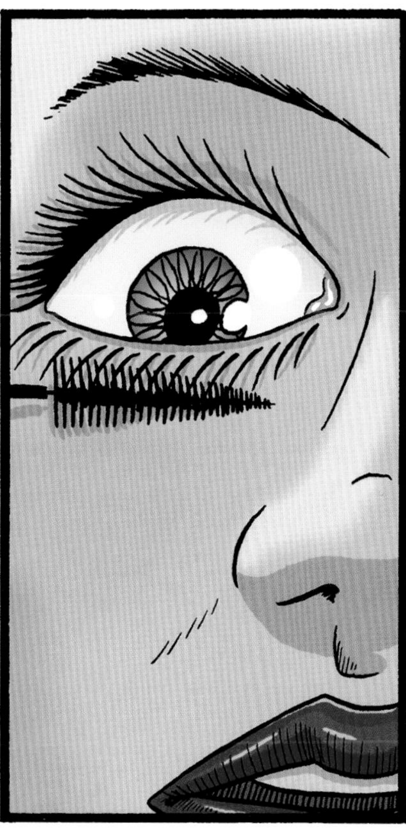

STEPHEN ELFORD

www.lemonadeillustration.com

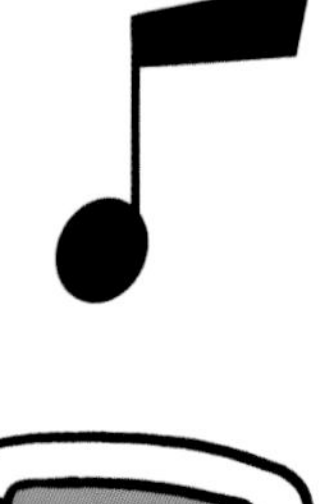

GARY SWIFT ANIMATION

www.lemonadeillustration.com

LEMONADE

ILLUSTRATION AGENCY // **VOICE :** 07891 390750 // **EMAIL :** INFO@LEMONADEILLUSTRATION.COM
WEB : LEMONADEILLUSTRATION.COM // **OFFICE :** HILL HOUSE, SUITE 231, 210 UPPER RICHMOND RD, LONDON //

GARY SWIFT

www.lemonadeillustration.com

LEMONADE

ILLUSTRATION AGENCY // **VOICE :** 07891 390750 // **EMAIL :** INFO@LEMONADEILLUSTRATION.COM
WEB : LEMONADEILLUSTRATION.COM // **OFFICE :** HILL HOUSE, SUITE 231, 210 UPPER RICHMOND RD, LONDON //

GARY NEWMAN

www.lemonadeillustration.com

LEMONADE

ILLUSTRATION AGENCY // **VOICE :** 07891 390750 // **EMAIL :** INFO@LEMONADEILLUSTRATION.COM
WEB : LEMONADEILLUSTRATION.COM // **OFFICE :** HILL HOUSE, SUITE 231, 210 UPPER RICHMOND RD, LONDON //

GARY NEWMAN

ROBERT LITTLEFORD

LEMONADE

ILLUSTRATION AGENCY // **VOICE :** 07891 390750 // **EMAIL :** INFO@LEMONADEILLUSTRATION.COM
WEB : LEMONADEILLUSTRATION.COM // **OFFICE :** HILL HOUSE, SUITE 231, 210 UPPER RICHMOND RD, LONDON //

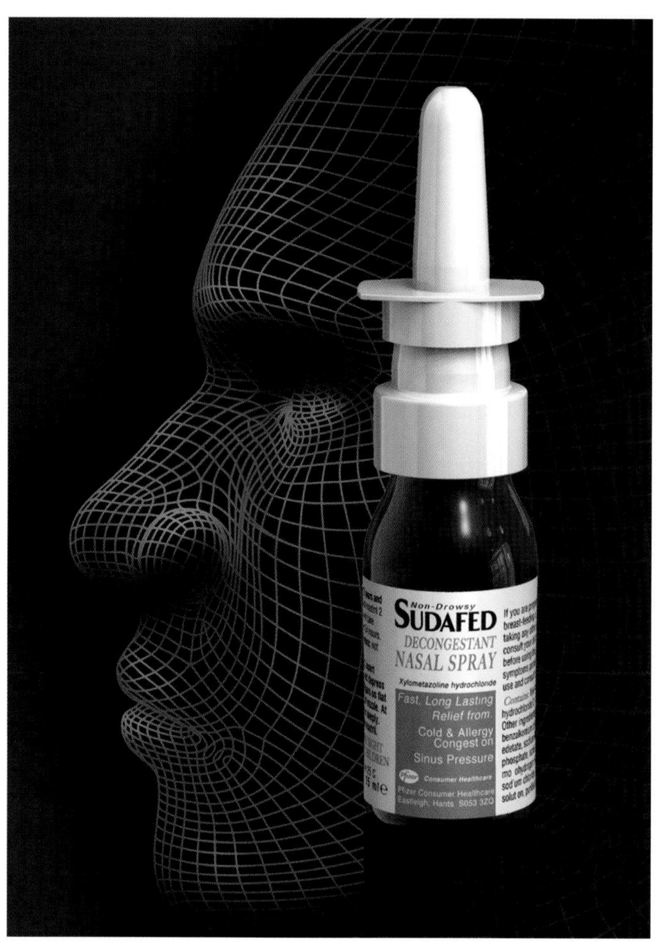

MATTHEW WHITE

www.lemonadeillustration.com

KATH WALKER

www.lemonadeillustration.com

DAVID SEMPLE

LEMONADE
ILLUSTRATION AGENCY // VOICE : 07891 390750 // EMAIL : INFO@LEMONADEILLUSTRATION.COM
WEB : LEMONADEILLUSTRATION.COM // OFFICE : HILL HOUSE, SUITE 231, 210 UPPER RICHMOND RD, LONDON //

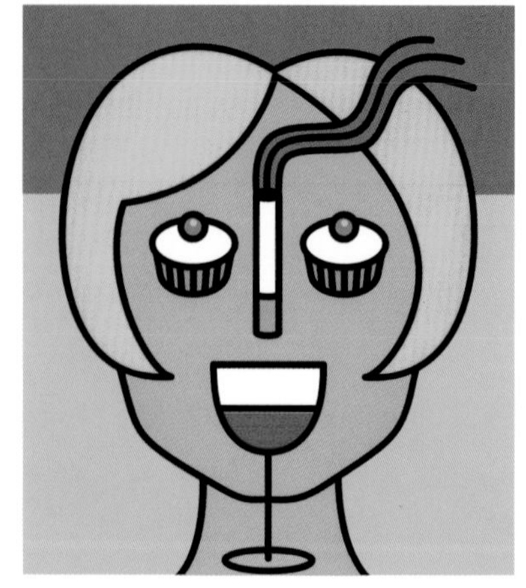

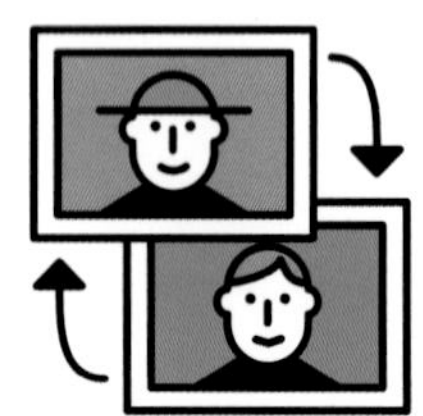

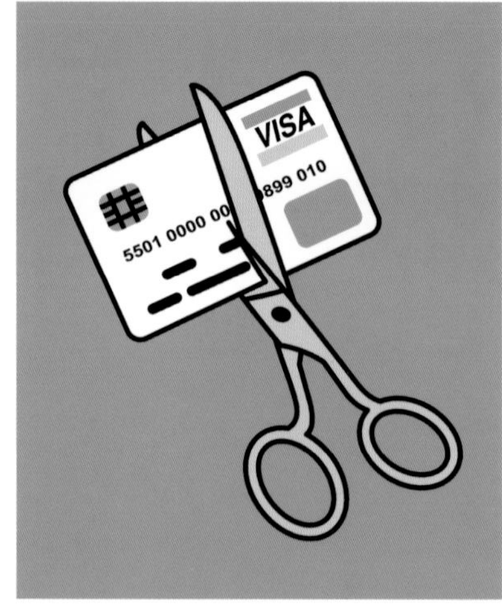

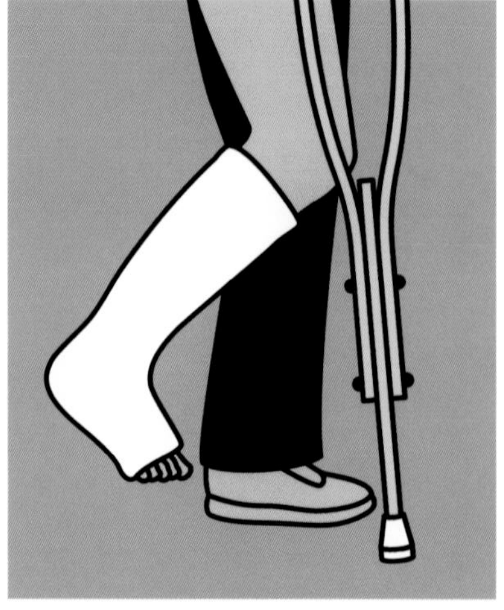

CYRUS DEBOO

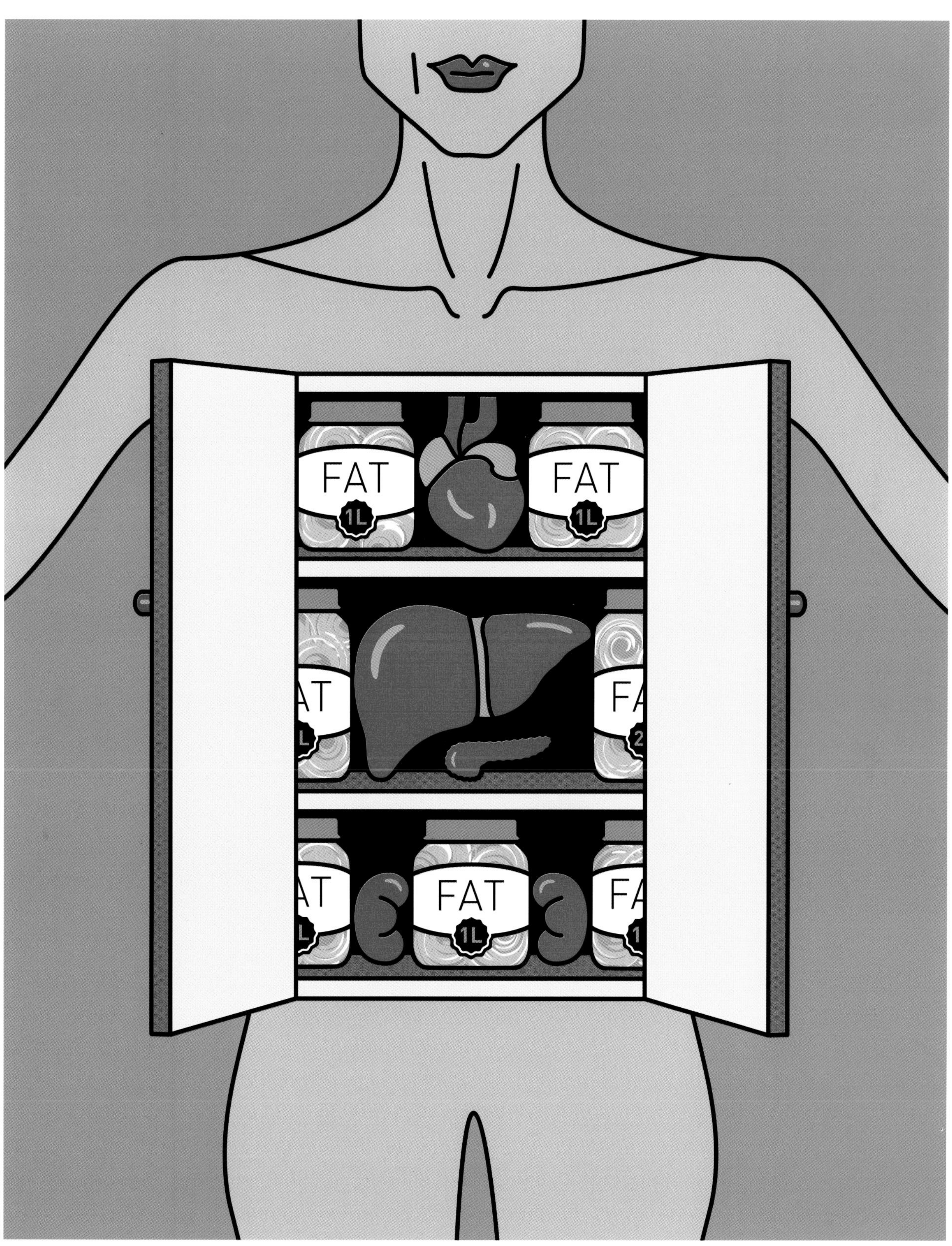

CYRUS DEBOO

www.lemonadeillustration.com

ANDREW PAINTER

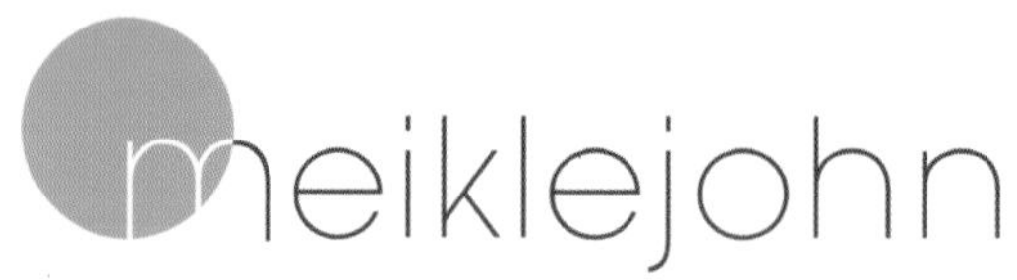

meiklejohn
5 Risborough Street London SE1 0HF
tel: +44 (0)20 7593 0500 fax: +44 (0)20 7593 0501 email: info@meiklejohn.co.uk www.meiklejohn.co.uk

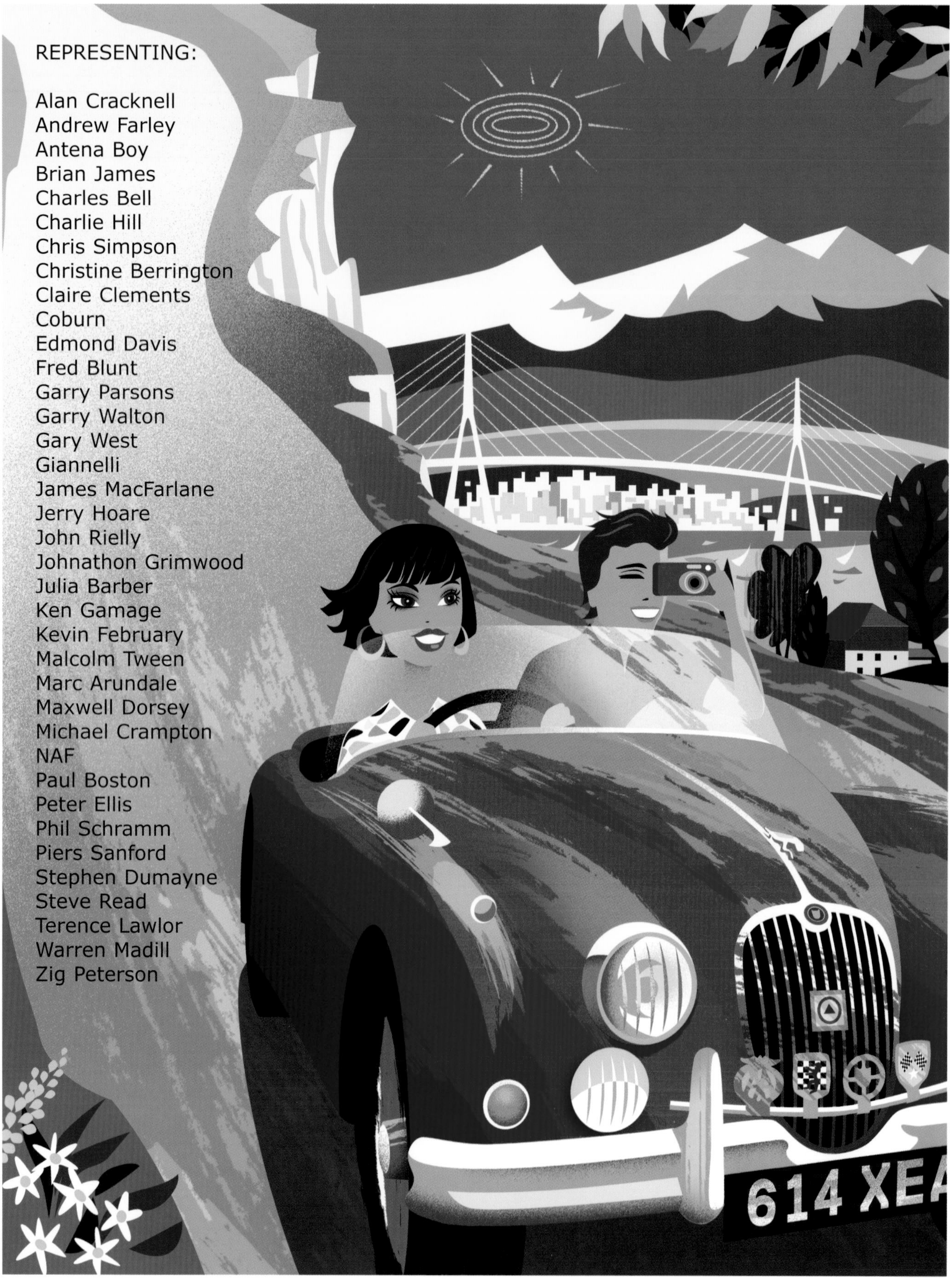
REPRESENTING:
Alan Cracknell
Andrew Farley
Antena Boy
Brian James
Charles Bell
Charlie Hill
Chris Simpson
Christine Berrington
Claire Clements
Coburn
Edmond Davis
Fred Blunt
Garry Parsons
Garry Walton
Gary West
Giannelli
James MacFarlane
Jerry Hoare
John Rielly
Johnathon Grimwood
Julia Barber
Ken Gamage
Kevin February
Malcolm Tween
Marc Arundale
Maxwell Dorsey
Michael Crampton
NAF
Paul Boston
Peter Ellis
Phil Schramm
Piers Sanford
Stephen Dumayne
Steve Read
Terence Lawlor
Warren Madill
Zig Peterson
614 XEA

MICHAEL CRAMPTON

www.meiklejohn.co.uk

5 Risborough Street London SE1 0HF
tel: +44 (0)20 7593 0500 fax: +44 (0)20 7593 0501 email: info@meiklejohn.co.uk www.meiklejohn.co.uk

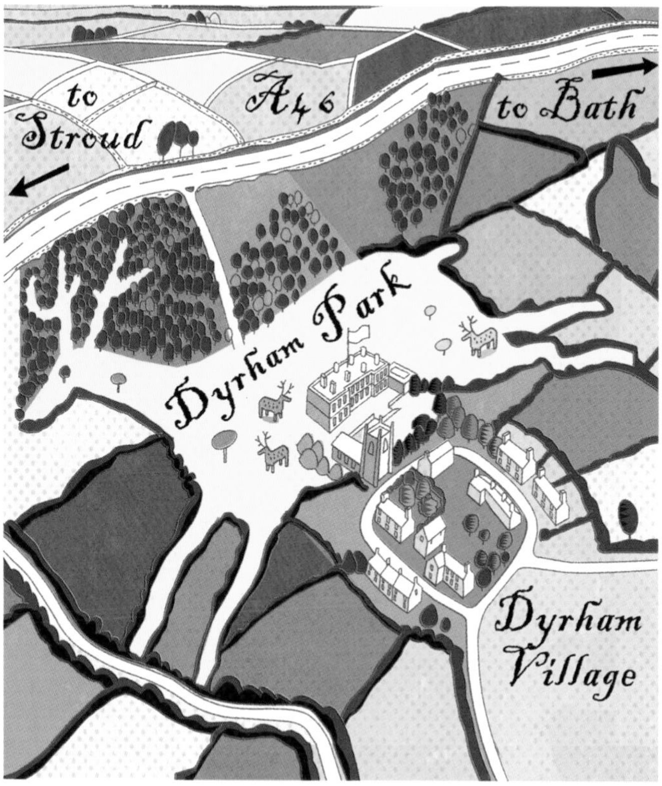

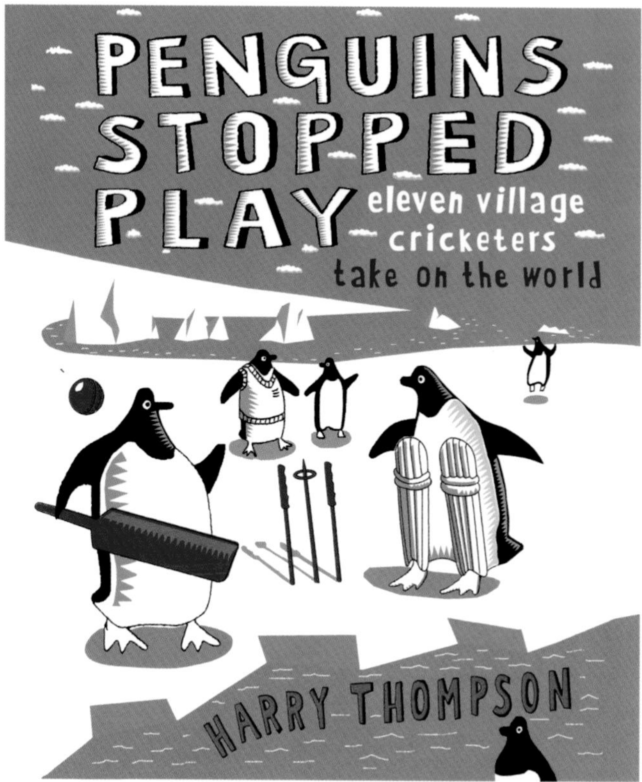

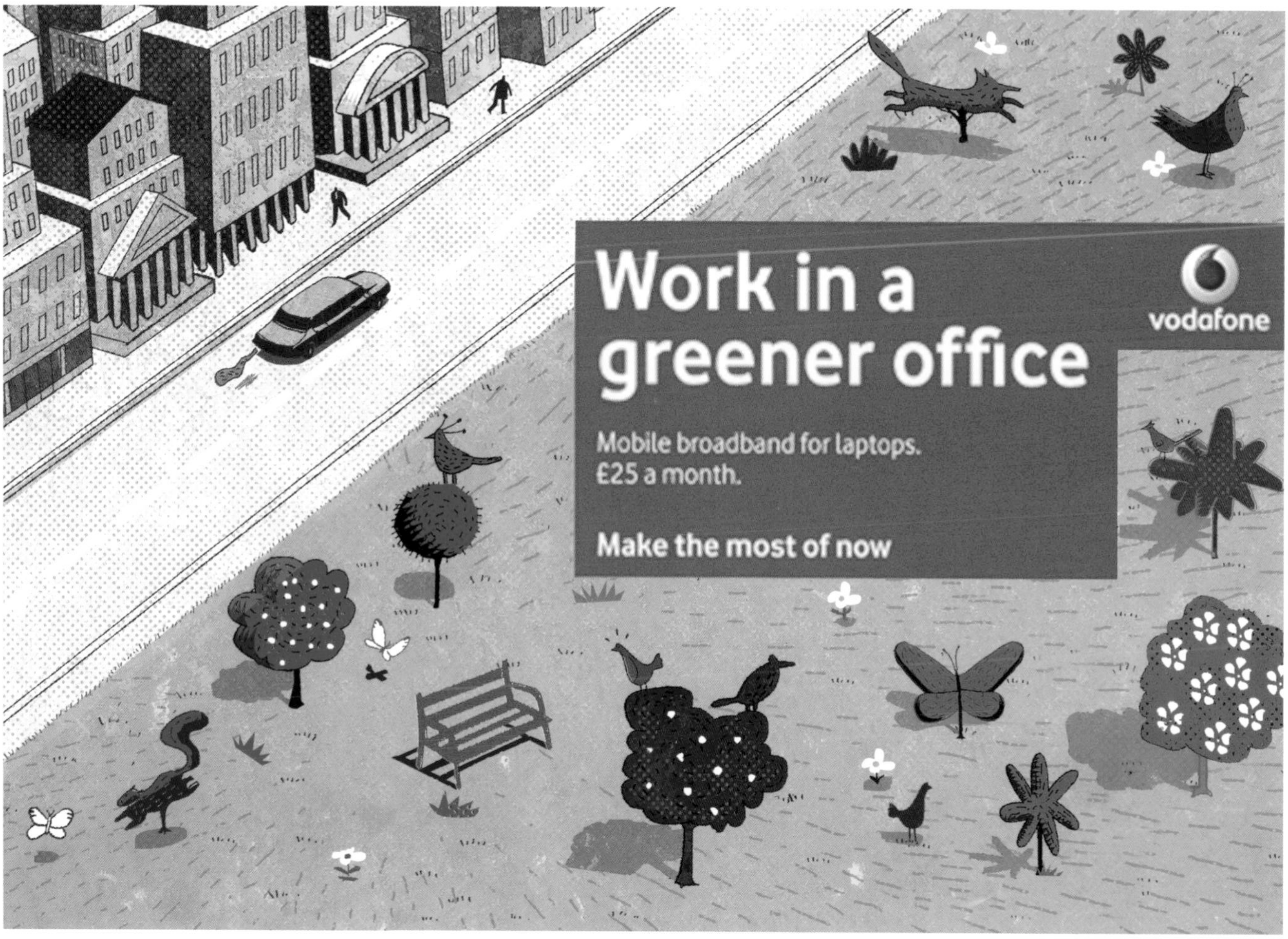

Work in a greener office

vodafone

Mobile broadband for laptops.
£25 a month.

Make the most of now

PAUL BOSTON

www.meiklejohn.co.uk

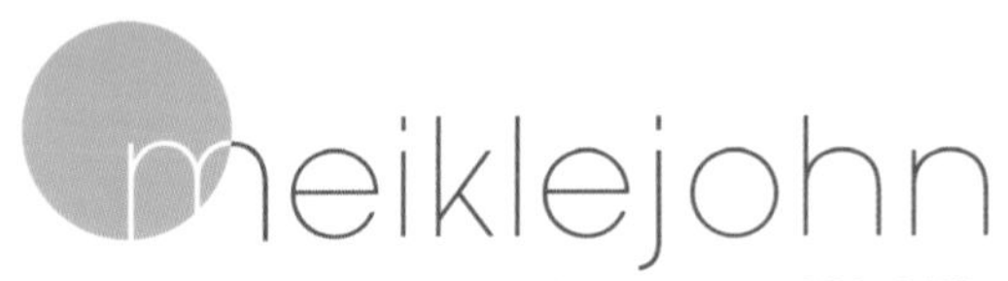

meiklejohn
5 Risborough Street London SE1 0HF
tel: +44 (0)20 7593 0500 fax: +44 (0)20 7593 0501 email: info@meiklejohn.co.uk www.meiklejohn.co.uk

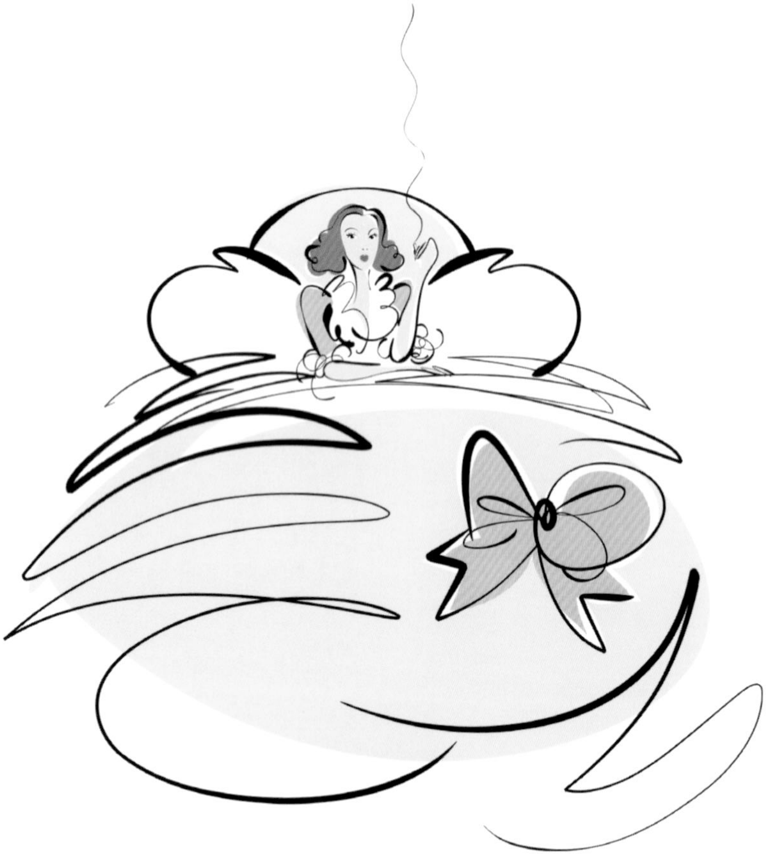

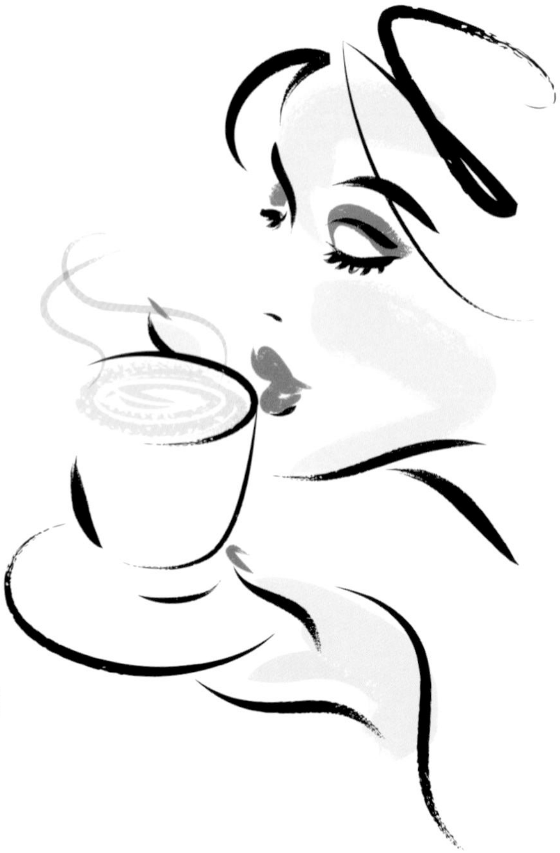

GIANNELLI

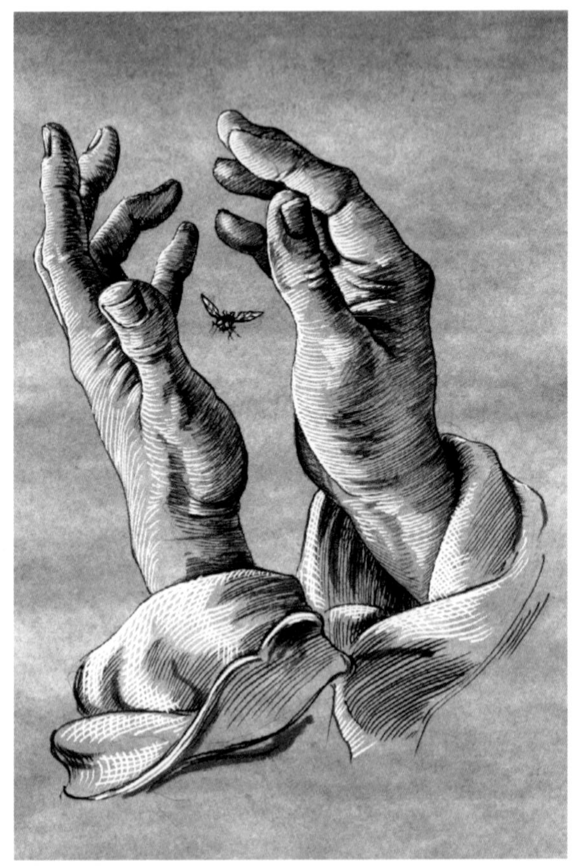

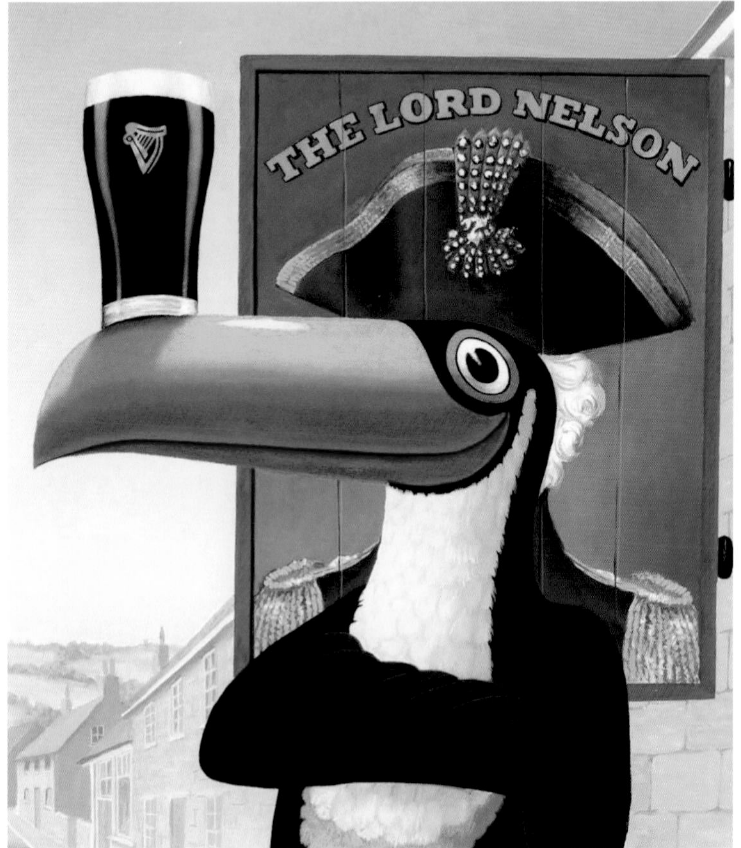

WARREN MADILL

5 Risborough Street London SE1 0HF
tel: +44 (0)20 7593 0500 fax: +44 (0)20 7593 0501 email: info@meiklejohn.co.uk www.meiklejohn.co.uk

COBURN

JULIA BARBER

www.meiklejohn.co.uk

5 Risborough Street London SE1 0HF
tel: +44 (0)20 7593 0500 fax: +44 (0)20 7593 0501 email: info@meiklejohn.co.uk www.meiklejohn.co.uk

GARRY WALTON

www.meiklejohn.co.uk

5 Risborough Street London SE1 0HF
tel: +44 (0)20 7593 0500 fax: +44 (0)20 7593 0501 email: info@meiklejohn.co.uk www.meiklejohn.co.uk

GARRY WALTON

www.meiklejohn.co.uk

5 Risborough Street London SE1 0HF

tel: +44 (0)20 7593 0500 fax: +44 (0)20 7593 0501 email: info@meiklejohn.co.uk www.meiklejohn.co.uk

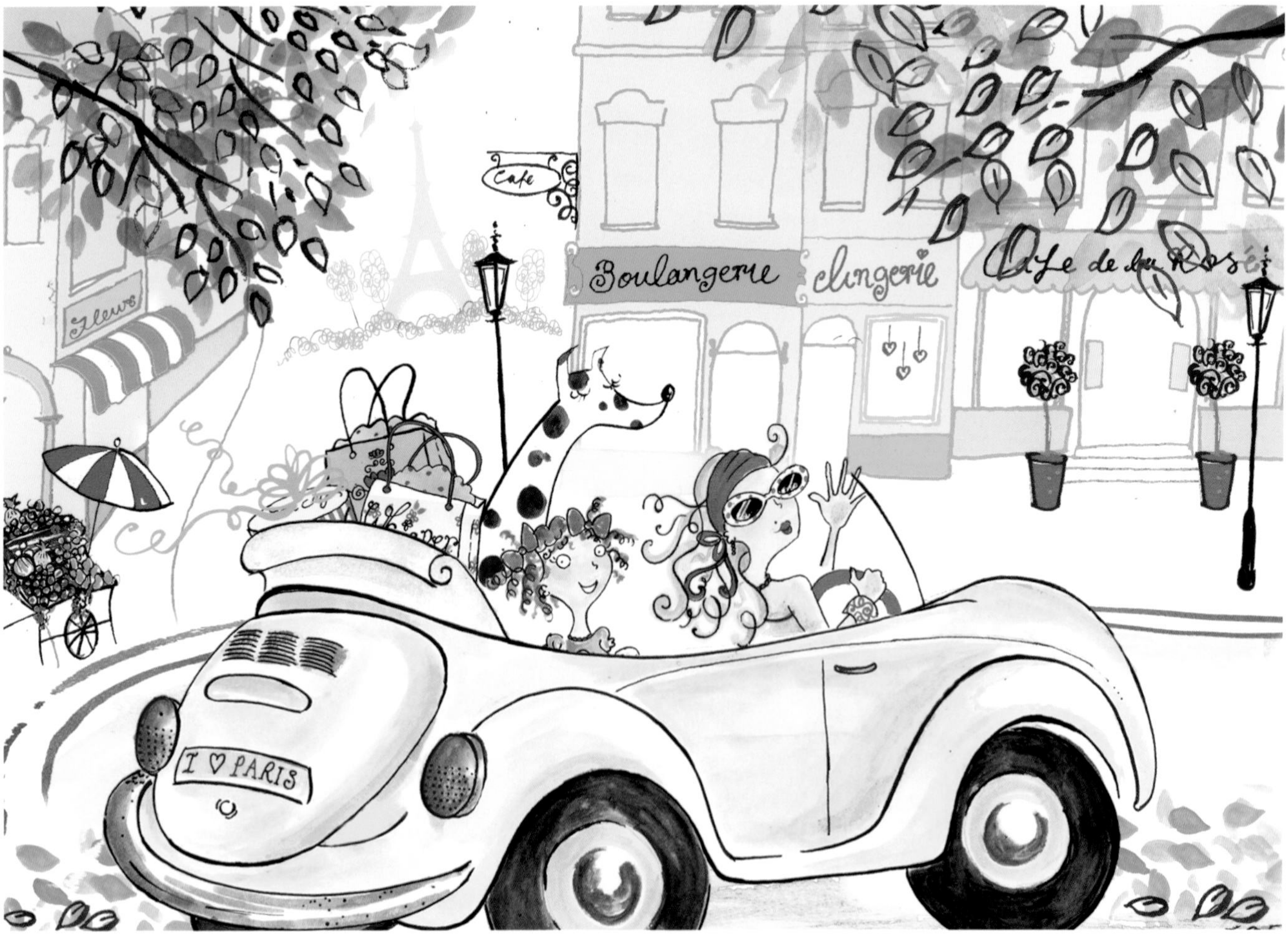

CLAIRE CLEMENTS

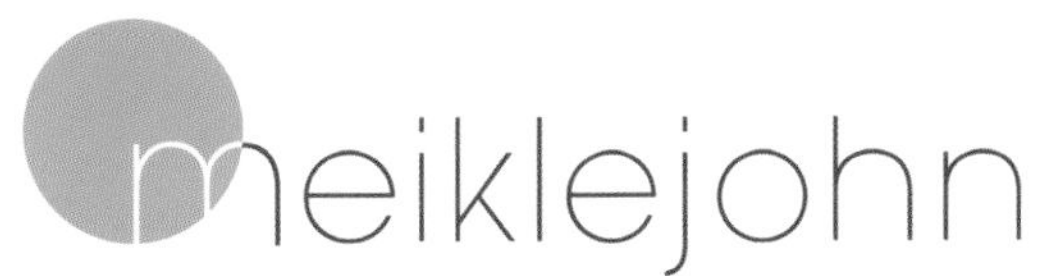

meiklejohn
5 Risborough Street London SE1 0HF
tel: +44 (0)20 7593 0500 fax: +44 (0)20 7593 0501 email: info@meiklejohn.co.uk www.meiklejohn.co.uk

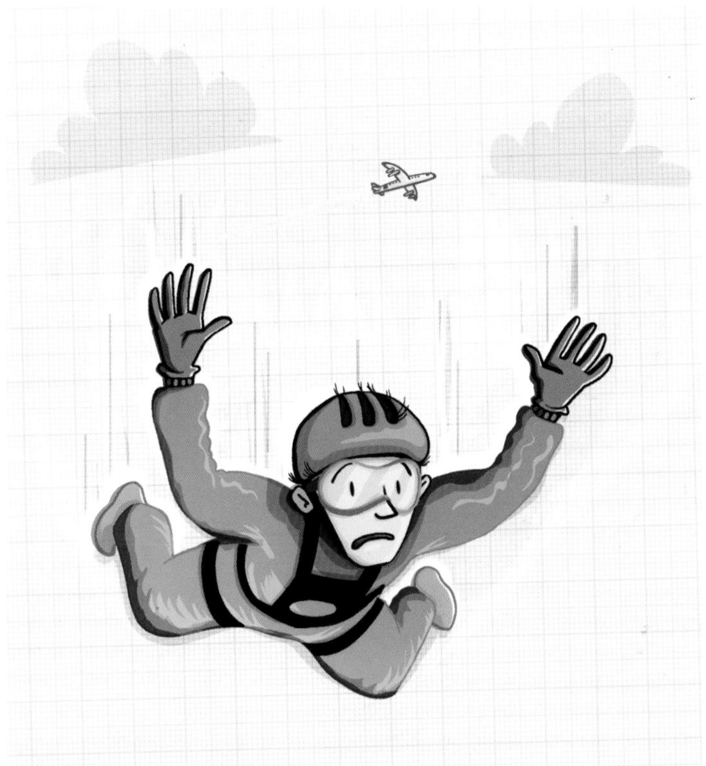

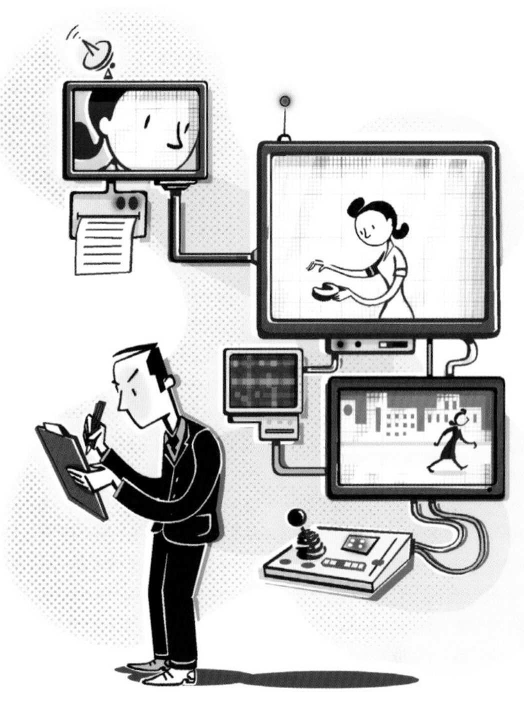

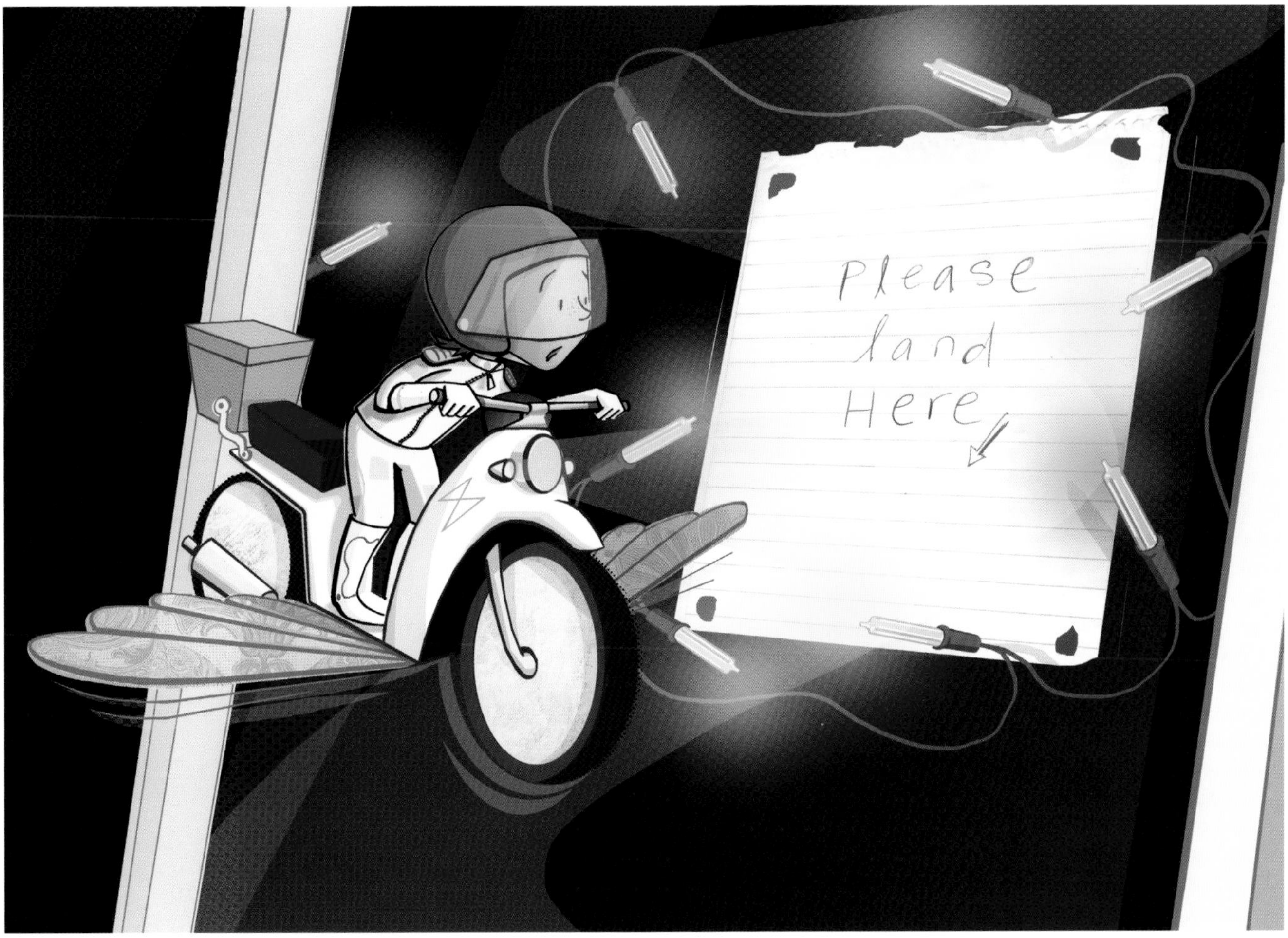

GARRY PARSONS

www.meiklejohn.co.uk

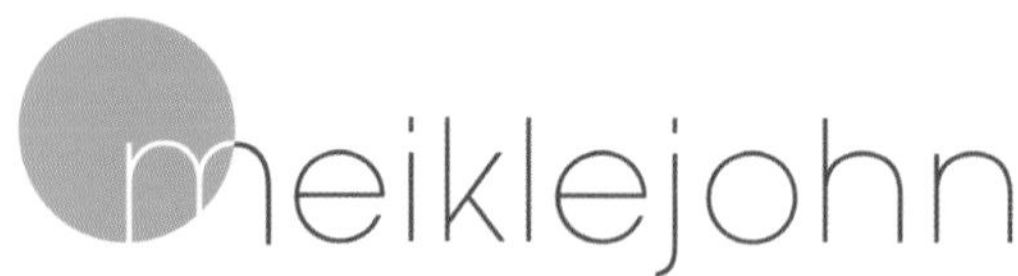

meiklejohn
5 Risborough Street London SE1 0HF
tel: +44 (0)20 7593 0500 fax: +44 (0)20 7593 0501 email: info@meiklejohn.co.uk www.meiklejohn.co.uk

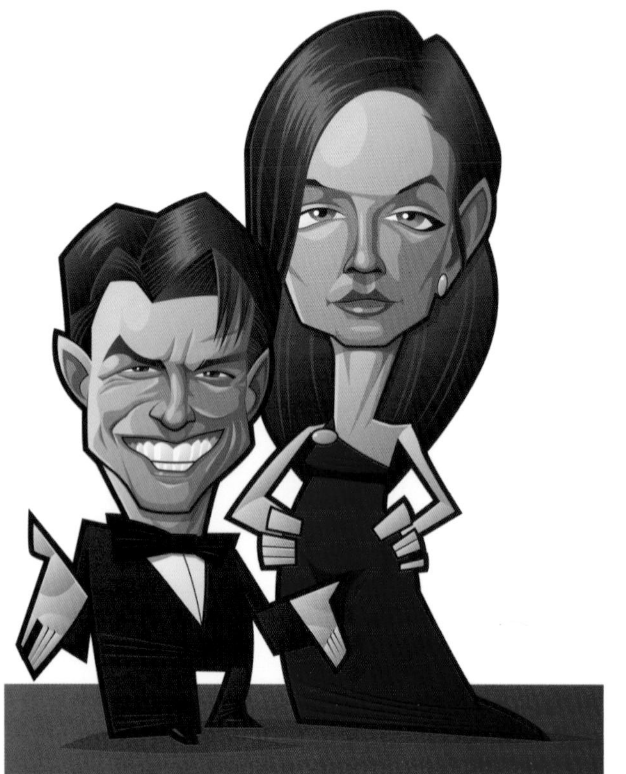

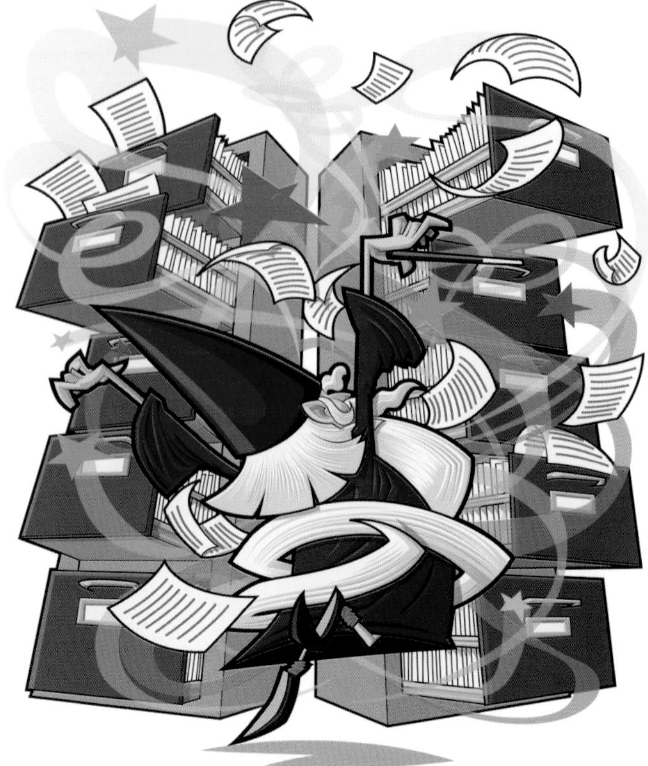

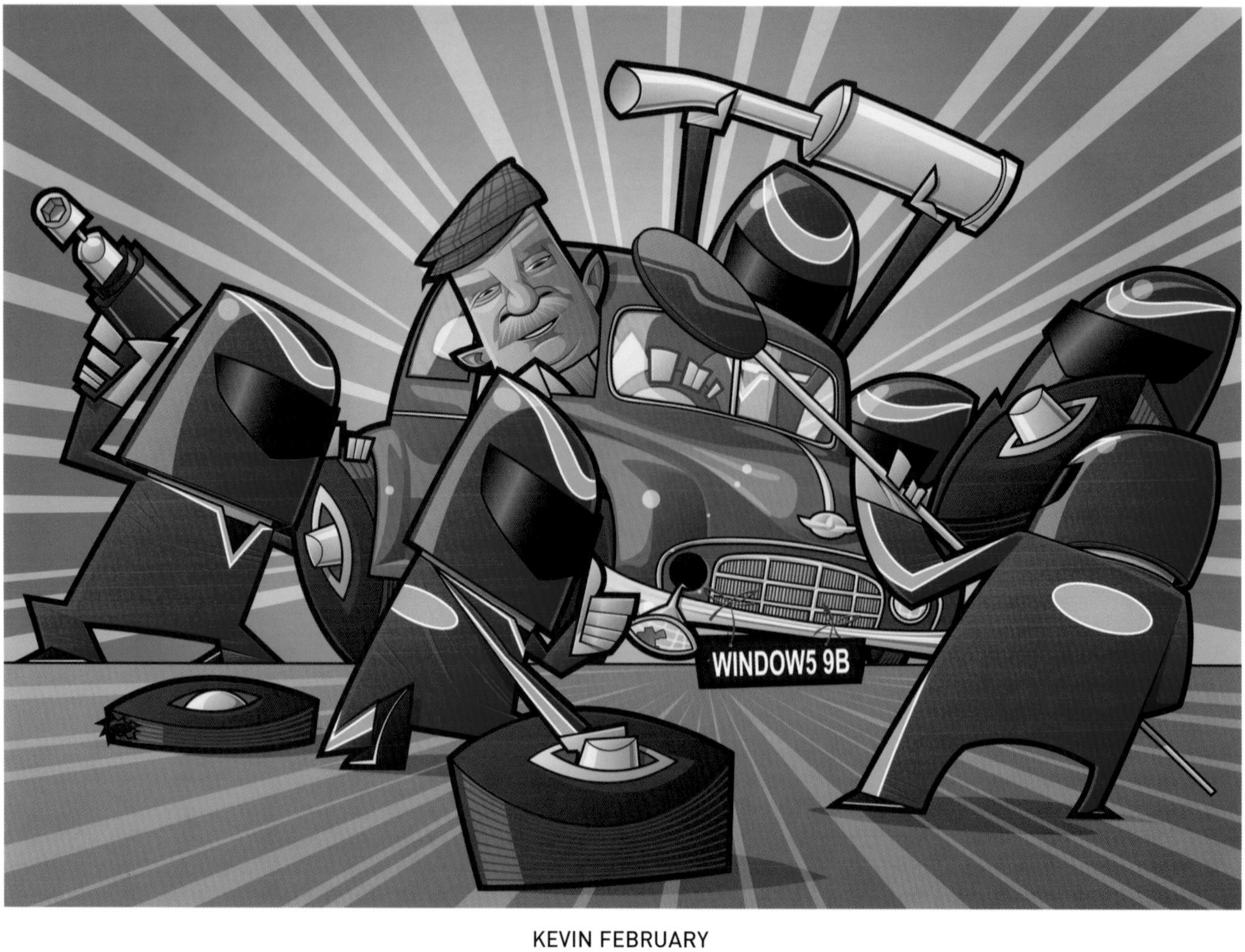

KEVIN FEBRUARY

5 Risborough Street London SE1 0HF
tel: +44 (0)20 7593 0500 fax: +44 (0)20 7593 0501 email: info@meiklejohn.co.uk www.meiklejohn.co.uk

ANDREW FARLEY

www.meiklejohn.co.uk

5 Risborough Street London SE1 0HF
tel: +44 (0)20 7593 0500 fax: +44 (0)20 7593 0501 email: info@meiklejohn.co.uk www.meiklejohn.co.uk

FRED BLUNT

www.meiklejohn.co.uk

TEL(+44)2072789131
FAX(+44)2072789121
NB
ILLUSTRATION
WWW.nbillustration.co.uk
info@nbillustration.co.uk
40 BOWLING GREEN LANE
CLERKENWELL
LONDON
EC1R0NE

NB ILLUSTRATION LTD 40 BOWLING GREEN LANE CLERKENWELL LONDON EC1R 0NE
T +44 020 7278 9131 **F** +44 020 7278 9121 **E** info@nbillustration.co.uk **W** www.nbillustration.co.uk

CAROLE VERBYST

www.nbillustration.co.uk

NB ILLUSTRATION LTD 40 BOWLING GREEN LANE CLERKENWELL LONDON EC1R 0NE
T +44 020 7278 9131 **F** +44 020 7278 9121 **E** info@nbillustration.co.uk **W** www.nbillustration.co.uk

LAURENCE WHITELEY

www.nbillustration.co.uk

NB ILLUSTRATION LTD 40 BOWLING GREEN LANE CLERKENWELL LONDON EC1R 0NE
T +44 020 7278 9131 **F** +44 020 7278 9121 **E** info@nbillustration.co.uk **W** www.nbillustration.co.uk

LAURENCE WHITELEY

www.nbillustration.co.uk

NB ILLUSTRATION LTD 40 BOWLING GREEN LANE CLERKENWELL LONDON EC1R 0NE
T +44 020 7278 9131 **F** +44 020 7278 9121 **E** info@nbillustration.co.uk **W** www.nbillustration.co.uk

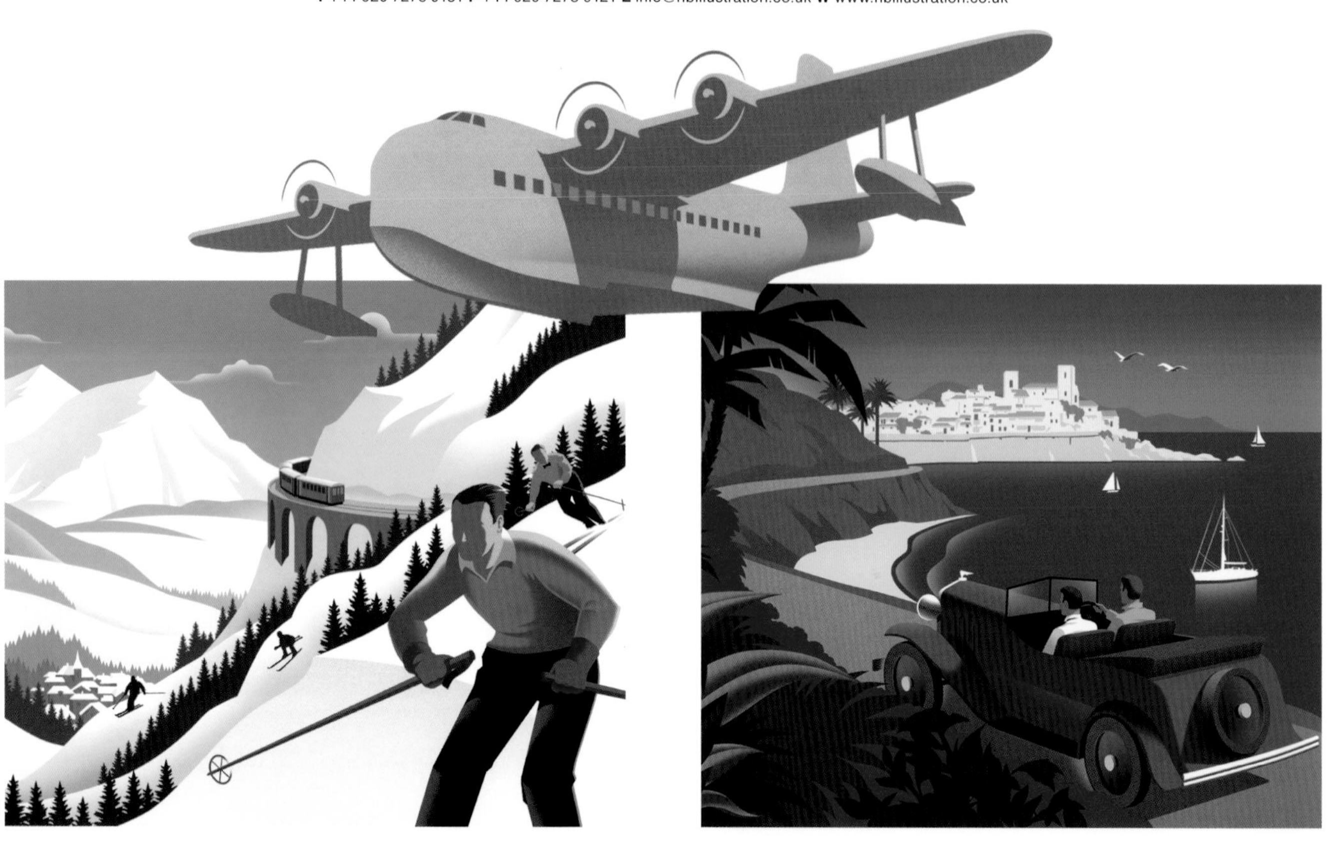

LAURENCE WHITELEY

www.nbillustration.co.uk

NB ILLUSTRATION LTD 40 BOWLING GREEN LANE CLERKENWELL LONDON EC1R 0NE
T +44 020 7278 9131 F +44 020 7278 9121 E info@nbillustration.co.uk W www.nbillustration.co.uk

CHRIS VINE

www.nbillustration.co.uk

NB ILLUSTRATION LTD 40 BOWLING GREEN LANE CLERKENWELL LONDON EC1R 0NE
T +44 020 7278 9131 **F** +44 020 7278 9121 **E** info@nbillustration.co.uk **W** www.nbillustration.co.uk

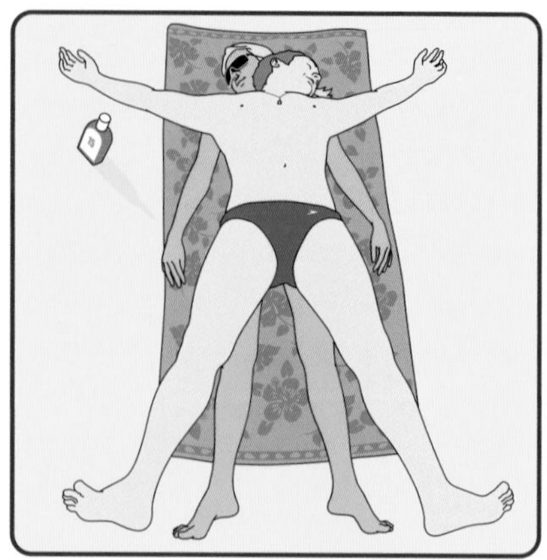

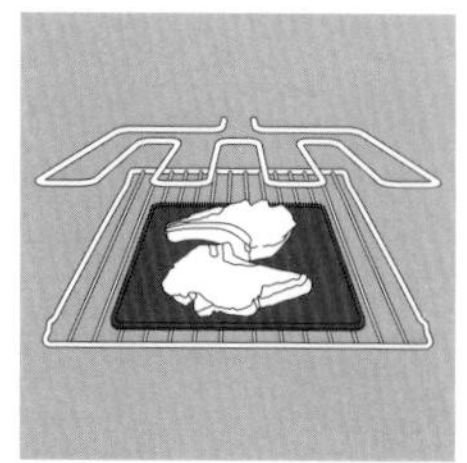

Smoked grass on the way to work

10 pints last night

5 pints, 6 whiskies and a gram of cocaine on a weekend binge

Smokes a few joints every evening

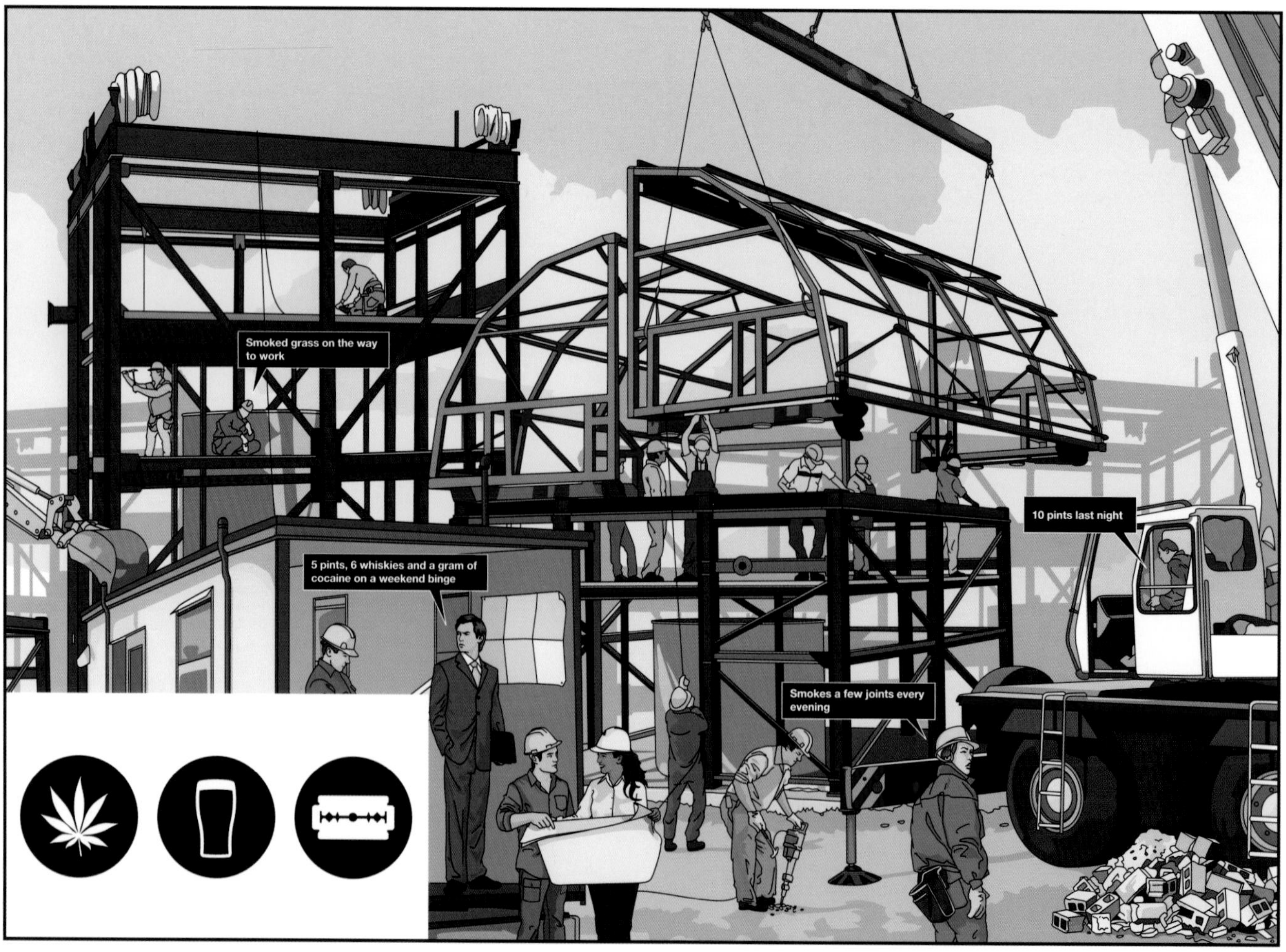

BEN HASLER

www.nbillustration.co.uk

NB ILLUSTRATION LTD 40 BOWLING GREEN LANE CLERKENWELL LONDON EC1R 0NE
T +44 020 7278 9131 **F** +44 020 7278 9121 **E** info@nbillustration.co.uk **W** www.nbillustration.co.uk

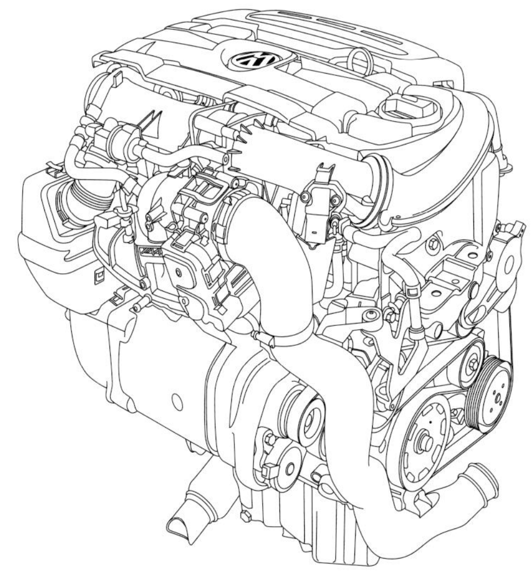

BEN HASLER

www.nbillustration.co.uk

NB ILLUSTRATION LTD 40 BOWLING GREEN LANE CLERKENWELL LONDON EC1R 0NE
T +44 020 7278 9131 **F** +44 020 7278 9121 **E** info@nbillustration.co.uk **W** www.nbillustration.co.uk

JONATHAN BURTON

www.nbillustration.co.uk

NB ILLUSTRATION LTD 40 BOWLING GREEN LANE CLERKENWELL LONDON EC1R 0NE
T +44 020 7278 9131 **F** +44 020 7278 9121 **E** info@nbillustration.co.uk **W** www.nbillustration.co.uk

JONATHAN BURTON

www.nbillustration.co.uk

NB ILLUSTRATION LTD 40 BOWLING GREEN LANE CLERKENWELL LONDON EC1R 0NE
T +44 020 7278 9131 **F** +44 020 7278 9121 **E** info@nbillustration.co.uk **W** www.nbillustration.co.uk

SARAH NAYLER

www.nbillustration.co.uk

NB ILLUSTRATION LTD 40 BOWLING GREEN LANE CLERKENWELL LONDON EC1R 0NE
T +44 020 7278 9131 **F** +44 020 7278 9121 **E** info@nbillustration.co.uk **W** www.nbillustration.co.uk

SARAH NAYLER

www.nbillustration.co.uk

NB ILLUSTRATION LTD 40 BOWLING GREEN LANE CLERKENWELL LONDON EC1R 0NE
T +44 020 7278 9131 **F** +44 020 7278 9121 **E** info@nbillustration.co.uk **W** www.nbillustration.co.uk

KEVIN WALDRON

www.nbillustration.co.uk

NB ILLUSTRATION LTD 40 BOWLING GREEN LANE CLERKENWELL LONDON EC1R 0NE
T +44 020 7278 9131 **F** +44 020 7278 9121 **E** info@nbillustration.co.uk **W** www.nbillustration.co.uk

MARK BEECH

www.nbillustration.co.uk

NB ILLUSTRATION LTD 40 BOWLING GREEN LANE CLERKENWELL LONDON EC1R 0NE
T +44 020 7278 9131 **F** +44 020 7278 9121 **E** info@nbillustration.co.uk **W** www.nbillustration.co.uk

PHIL WRIGGLESWORTH

www.nbillustration.co.uk

NB ILLUSTRATION LTD 40 BOWLING GREEN LANE CLERKENWELL LONDON EC1R 0NE
T +44 020 7278 9131 **F** +44 020 7278 9121 **E** info@nbillustration.co.uk **W** www.nbillustration.co.uk

JUDY STEVENS

www.nbillustration.co.uk

nb illustration

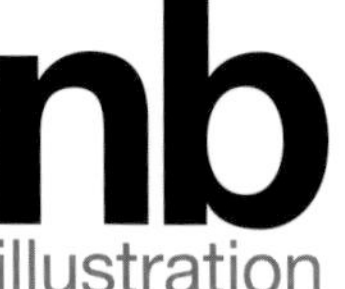

NB ILLUSTRATION LTD 40 BOWLING GREEN LANE CLERKENWELL LONDON EC1R 0NE
T +44 020 7278 9131 **F** +44 020 7278 9121 **E** info@nbillustration.co.uk **W** www.nbillustration.co.uk

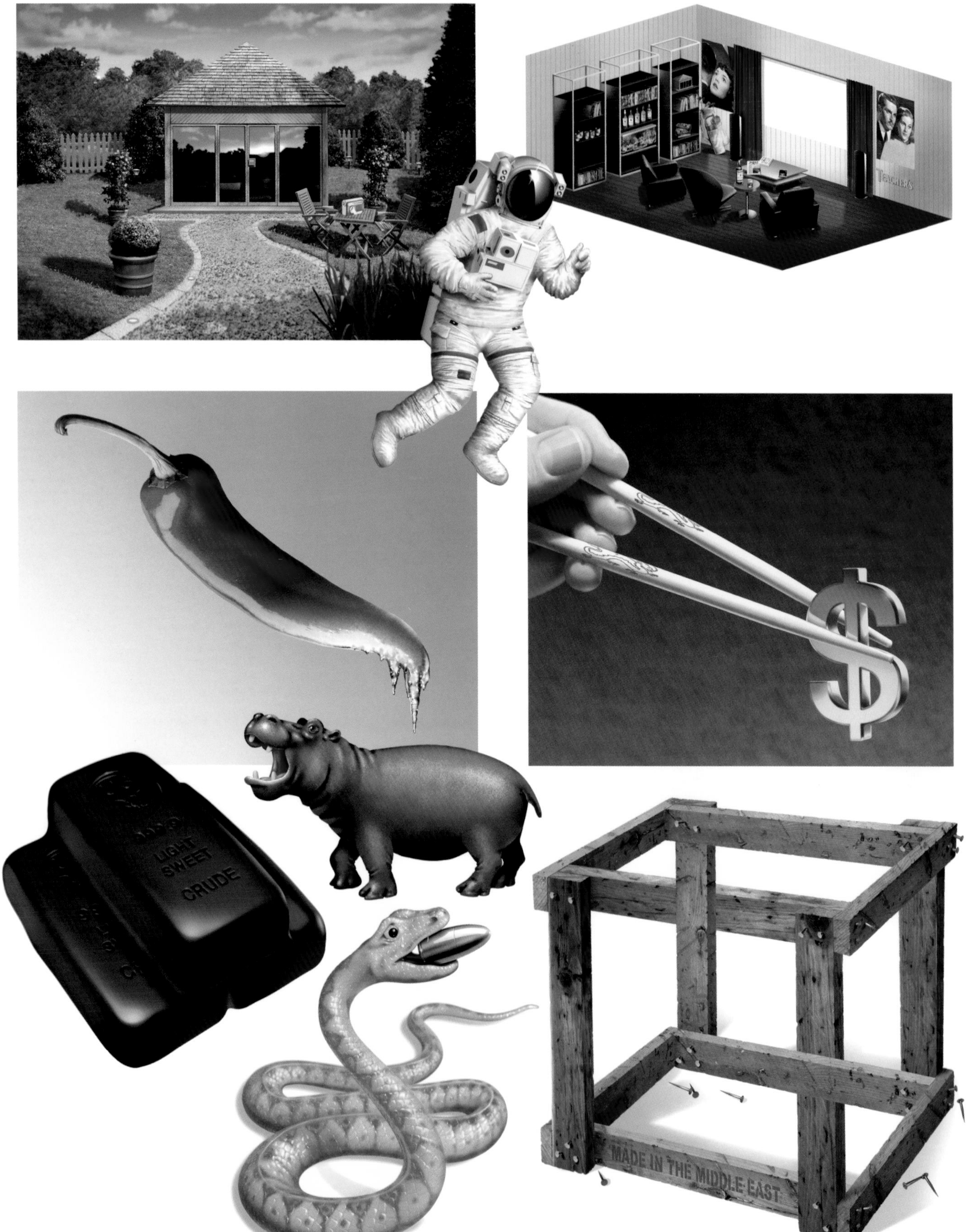

RICHARD DUCKETT

www.nbillustration.co.uk

NB ILLUSTRATION LTD 40 BOWLING GREEN LANE CLERKENWELL LONDON EC1R 0NE
T +44 020 7278 9131 **F** +44 020 7278 9121 **E** info@nbillustration.co.uk **W** www.nbillustration.co.uk

MARTIN & CHARLOTTE MACRAE

www.nbillustration.co.uk

NB ILLUSTRATION LTD 40 BOWLING GREEN LANE CLERKENWELL LONDON EC1R 0NE
T +44 020 7278 9131 **F** +44 020 7278 9121 **E** info@nbillustration.co.uk **W** www.nbillustration.co.uk

IVAN GILLETT

SIMON STEPHENSON

NB ILLUSTRATION LTD 40 BOWLING GREEN LANE CLERKENWELL LONDON EC1R 0NE
T +44 020 7278 9131 **F** +44 020 7278 9121 **E** info@nbillustration.co.uk **W** www.nbillustration.co.uk

BEVERLEY YOUNG

IAN PHILLIPS

NB ILLUSTRATION LTD 40 BOWLING GREEN LANE CLERKENWELL LONDON EC1R 0NE
T +44 020 7278 9131 **F** +44 020 7278 9121 **E** info@nbillustration.co.uk **W** www.nbillustration.co.uk

DAVID YOUNG

CHRIS COADY

NB ILLUSTRATION LTD 40 BOWLING GREEN LANE CLERKENWELL LONDON EC1R 0NE
T +44 020 7278 9131 **F** +44 020 7278 9121 **E** info@nbillustration.co.uk **W** www.nbillustration.co.uk

DAVID MCALLISTER

DAVID ATKINSON

nb illustration

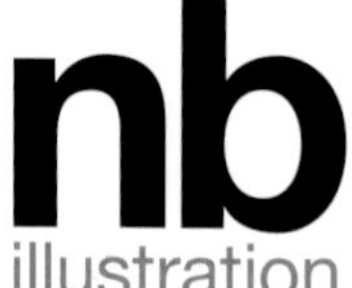

NB ILLUSTRATION LTD 40 BOWLING GREEN LANE CLERKENWELL LONDON EC1R 0NE
T +44 020 7278 9131 **F** +44 020 7278 9121 **E** info@nbillustration.co.uk **W** www.nbillustration.co.uk

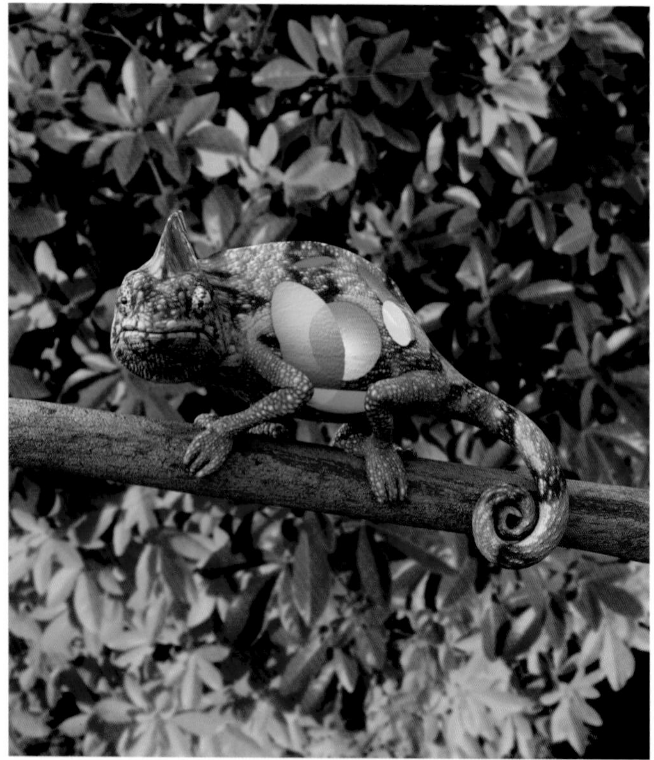

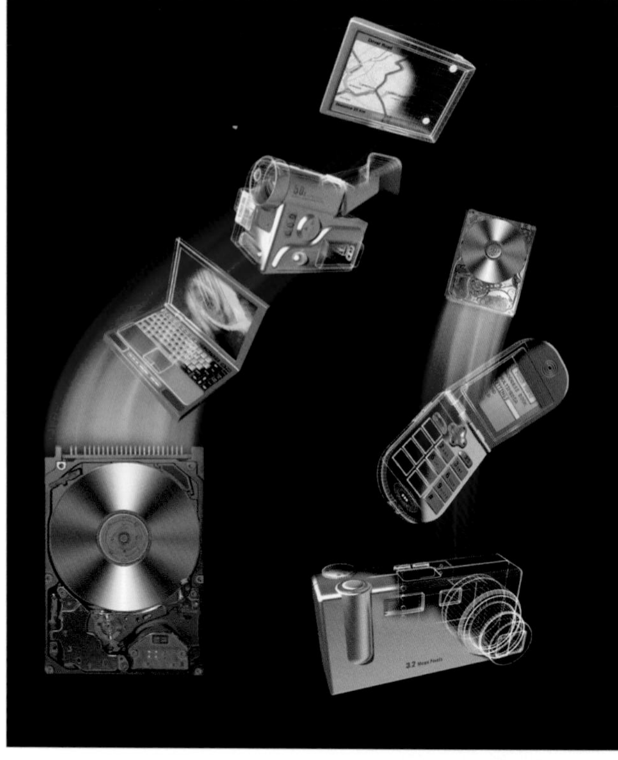

ROGER HARRIS

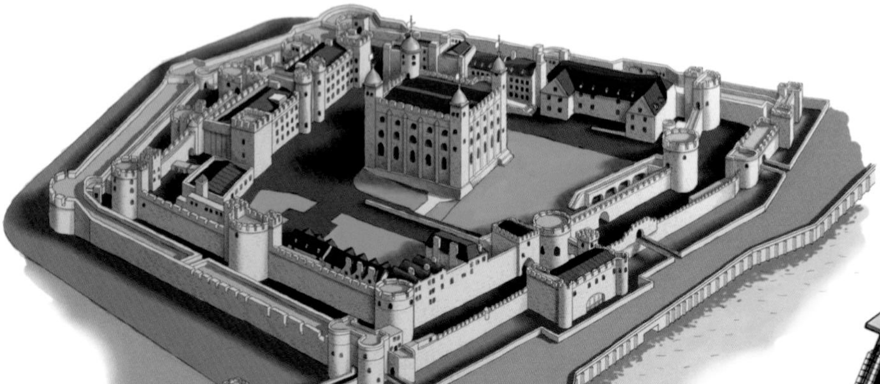

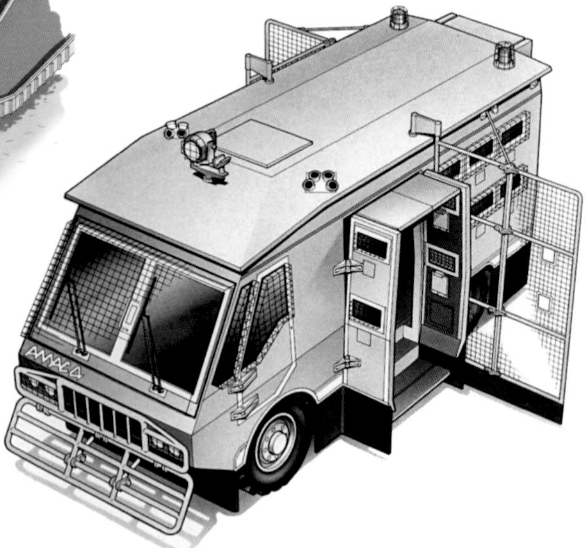

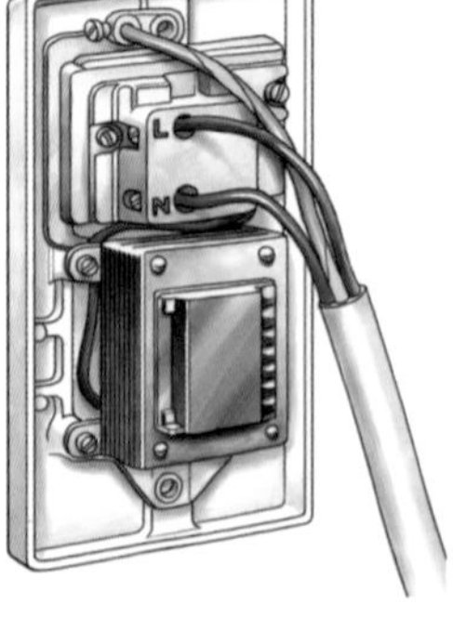

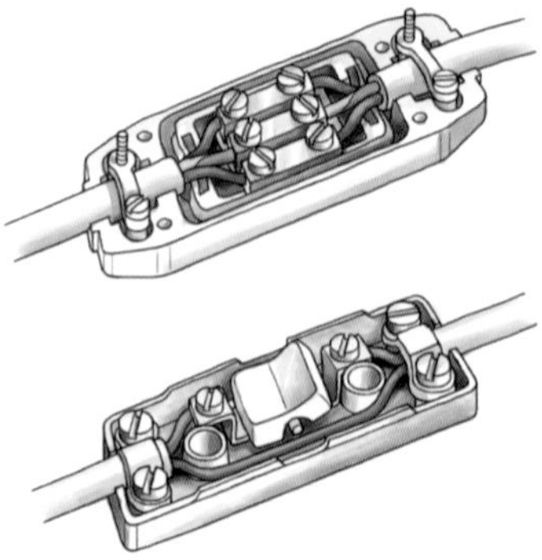

GRAHAM WHITE

new division

5 risborough street London se1 0hf

t:+44 (0)20 7593 0505 f:+44 (0)20 7593 0501 info@newdivision.com www.newdivision.com

Representing:

Nila Aye
Mark Blade
Glyn Brewerton
James Brown
Emma Brownjohn
Nicola Cramp
Chambers & Dorsey
Sophie Dupasquier
Jessie Eckel
Adam Errington
Melvyn Evans
Martina Farrow
Natalie Ferstendik
Anna Hymas
Helen James
Gary Kempston
Joanna Kerr
Mary Kilvert
Nick Kobyluch
Monica Laita
Jim Laurence
Yvonne Maxwell
Moira Millman
Clare Nicholas
Belinda Pearce
Gavin Reece
Suzanne Sales
Sean Sims
Barbara Spoettel
Lucy Truman
Katie Wood

BARBARA SPOETTEL

www.newdivision.com

5 risborough street london se1 0hf
t:+44 (0)20 7593 0505 f:+44 (0)20 7593 0501 info@newdivision.com www.newdivision.com

LUCY TRUMAN

www.newdivision.com

5 risborough street London se1 0hf
t:+44 (0)20 7593 0505 f:+44 (0)20 7593 0501 info@newdivision.com www.newdivision.com

ANNA HYMAS

www.newdivision.com

5 risborough street london se1 0hf
new division
t:+44 (0)20 7593 0505 f:+44 (0)20 7593 0501 info@newdivision.com www.newdivision.com

MELVYN EVANS

www.newdivision.com

new division

5 risborough street London se1 0hf
t:+44 (0)20 7593 0505 f:+44 (0)20 7593 0501 info@newdivision.com www.newdivision.com

GAVIN REECE

www.newdivision.com

5 risborough street london se1 0hf
new division
t:+44 (0)20 7593 0505 f:+44 (0)20 7593 0501 info@newdivision.com www.newdivision.com

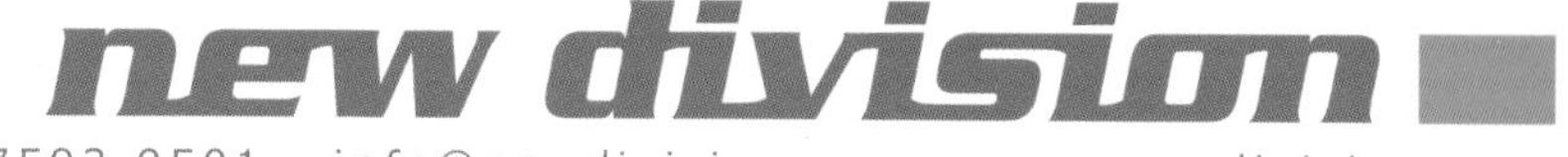

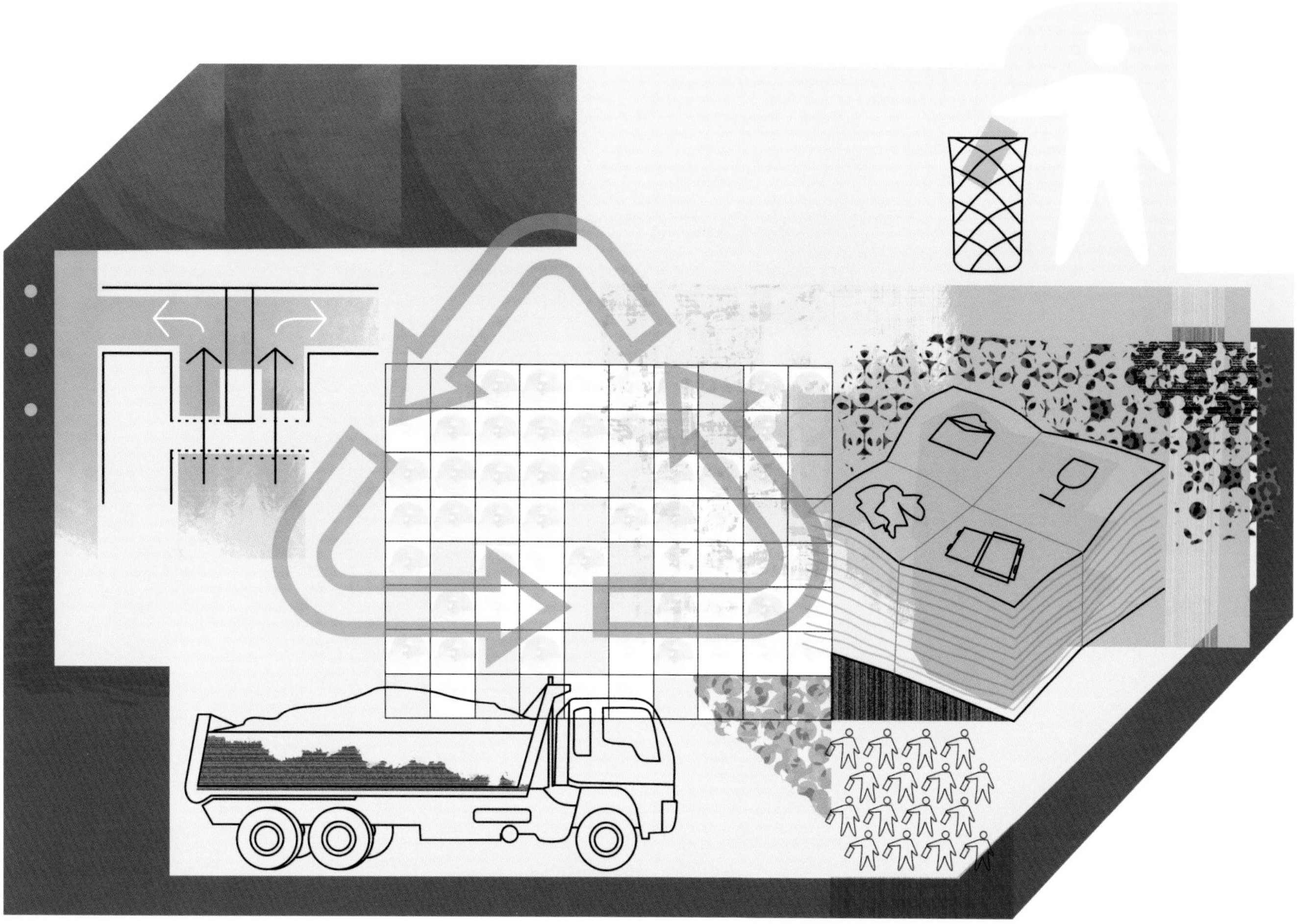

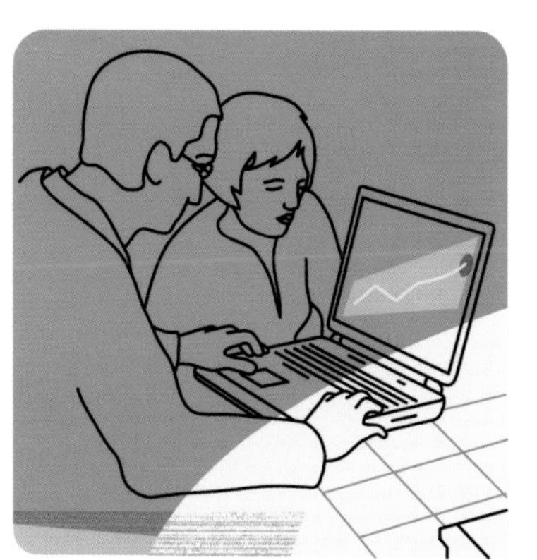

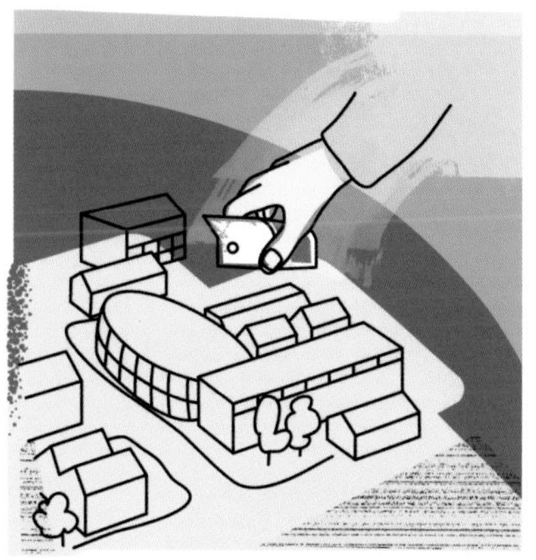

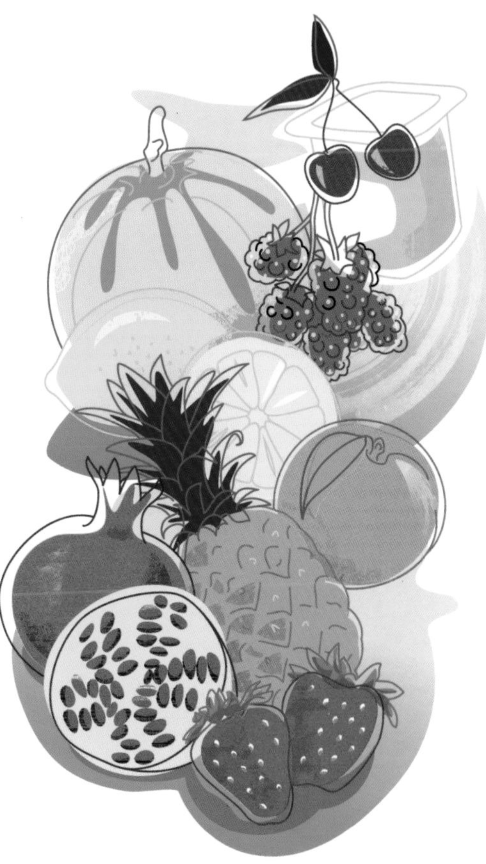

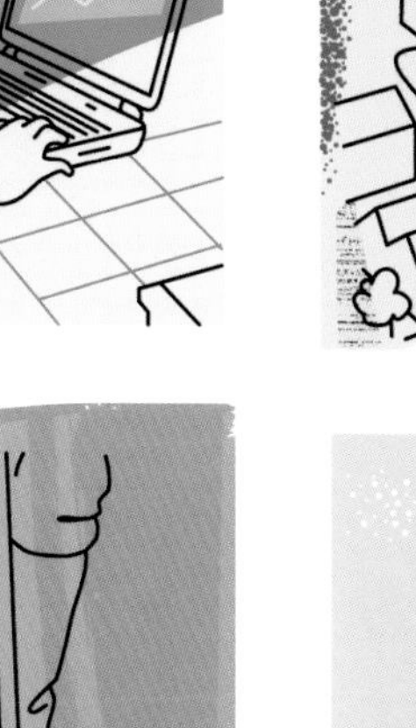

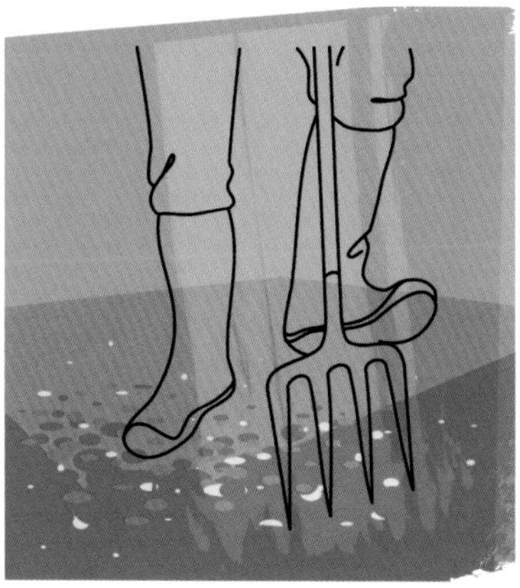

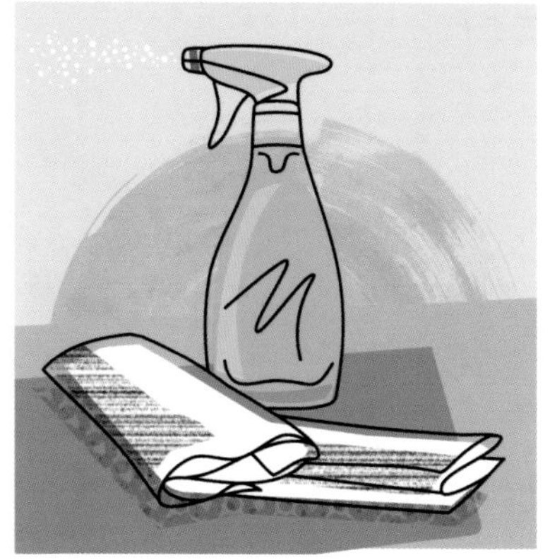

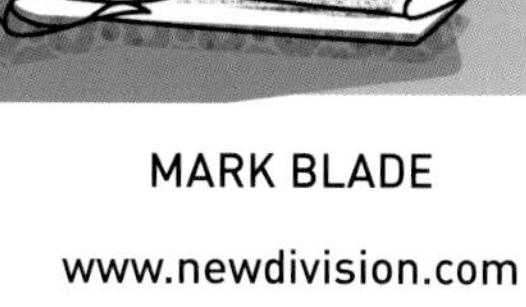

MARK BLADE

www.newdivision.com

new division
5 risborough street London se1 0hf
t:+44 (0)20 7593 0505 f:+44 (0)20 7593 0501 info@newdivision.com www.newdivision.com

SEAN SIMS

www.newdivision.com

5 risborough street london se1 0hf
new division
t:+44 (0)20 7593 0505 f:+44 (0)20 7593 0501 info@newdivision.com www.newdivision.com

JAMES BROWN

MARY KILVERT

new division 5 risborough street London se1 0hf
t:+44 (0)20 7593 0505 f:+44 (0)20 7593 0501 info@newdivision.com www.newdivision.com

JESSIE ECKEL

www.newdivision.com

5 risborough street london se1 0hf
t:+44 (0)20 7593 0505 f:+44 (0)20 7593 0501 info@newdivision.com www.newdivision.com

new division

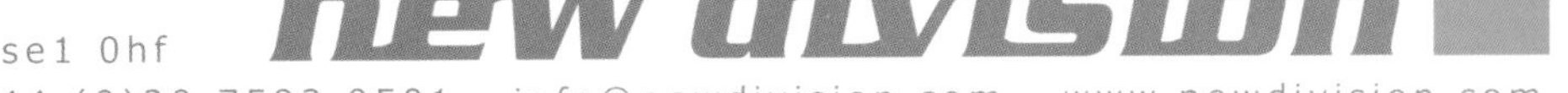

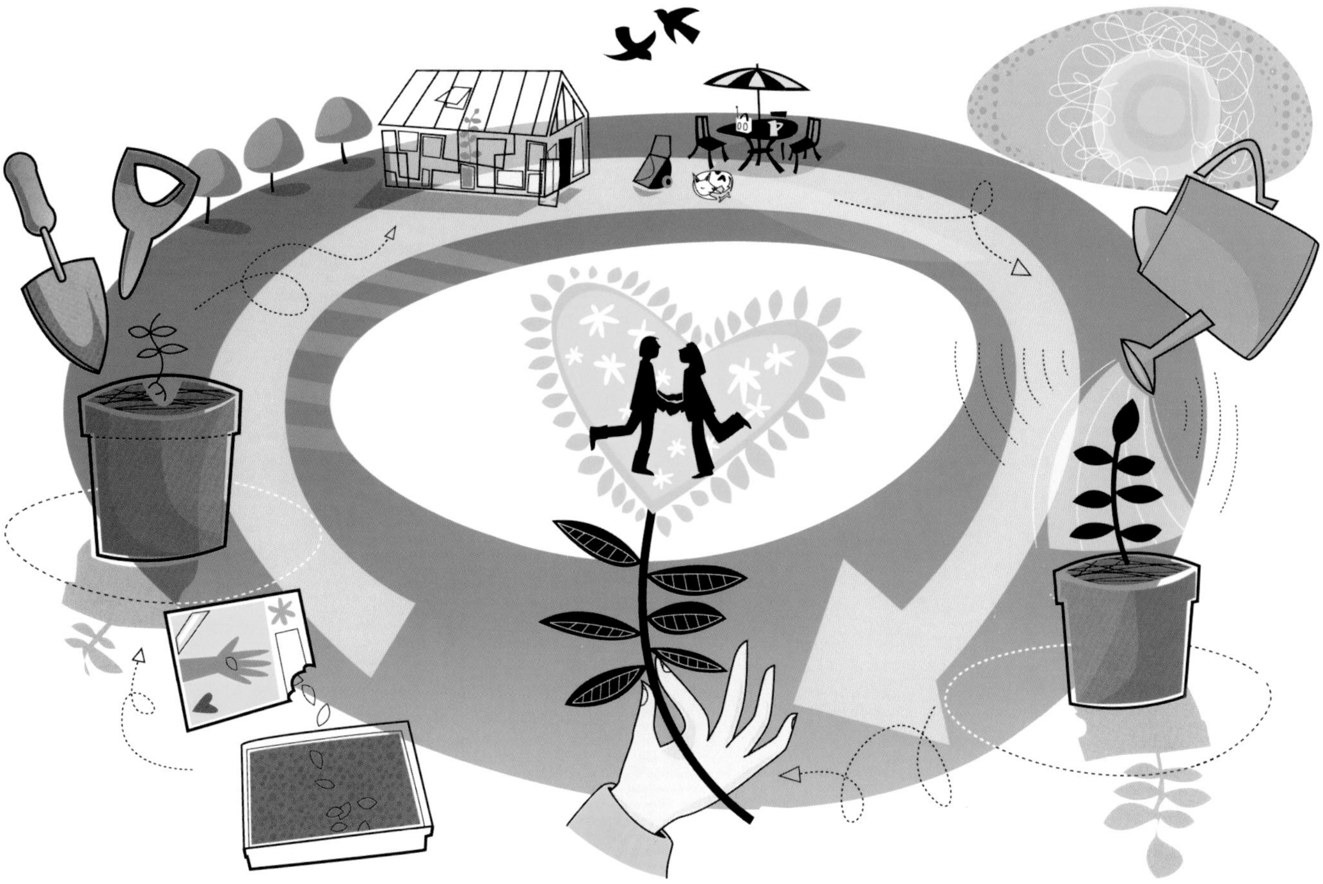

JOANNA KERR

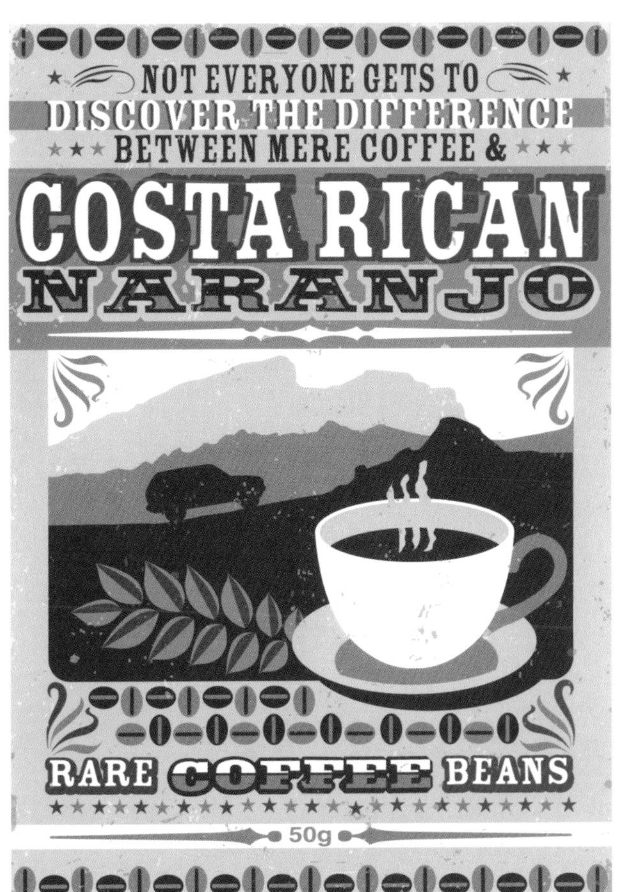

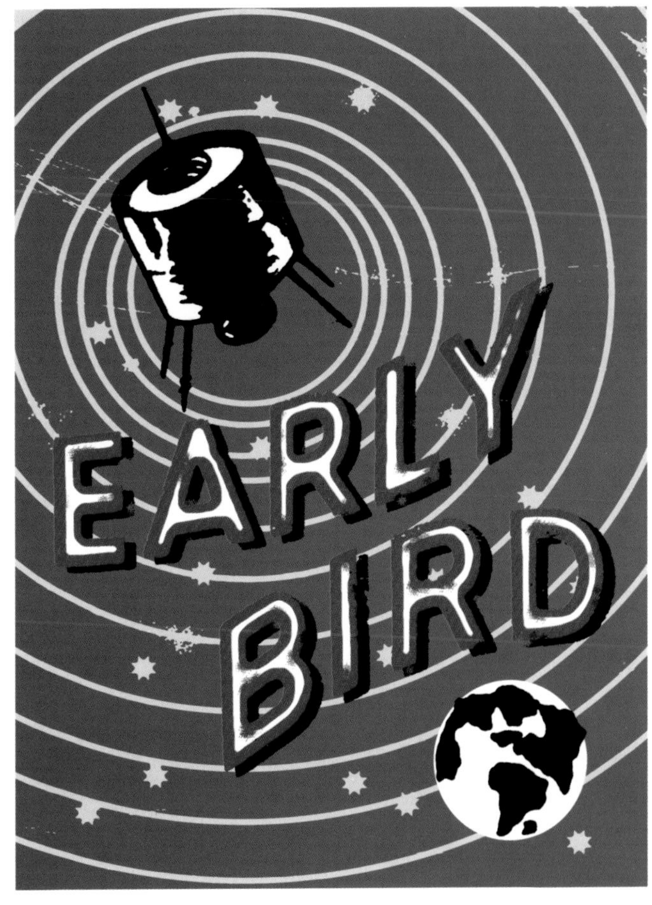

JIM LAURENCE

5 risborough street London se1 0hf
t:+44 (0)20 7593 0505 f:+44 (0)20 7593 0501 info@newdivision.com www.newdivision.com

NILA AYE

www.newdivision.com

new division
5 risborough street london se1 0hf
t:+44 (0)20 7593 0505 f:+44 (0)20 7593 0501 info@newdivision.com www.newdivision.com

MONICA LAITA

www.newdivision.com

new division 5 risborough street London se1 0hf
t:+44 (0)20 7593 0505 f:+44 (0)20 7593 0501 info@newdivision.com www.newdivision.com

MARTINA FARROW

www.newdivision.com

PHOSPHORART.COM

41 Pump House Close, London SE16 7HS tel:+44 (0)20 7064 4666 fax:+44 (0)20 7064 4660 email:info@phosphorart.com

REPRESENTING:

Anthony Atkinson
Alan Austin
Gerry Baptist
Mike Bell
John Blackford
Yulia Brodskaya
Linda Clark
Flammetta
Mandy Field
Claire Fletcher
Bill Garland
Keith Hagan
Giles Hargreaves
Paul Higgens
Dave Hopkins
Jib Hunt
Sandra Isaksson
Luc Janin
Mike Jarosko
Jennie
Nathan Jurevicius
Satoshi Kambayashi
Brian McIntyre
Dom Mimms
George Morton-Clark
Gail Newey
Christopher Nielson
David Nichols
Paul Ogilsby
Jon Rogers
Bill Sanderson
Silje Camilla Hellesen
Pete Viccars
Keith Watts
Julia Whatley
Richard Wetherill
Darren Whittington
Bob Wilson
Jonathan Wright

PHOSPHOR ART

GOES TO THE MOVIES

Check out our illustrators' work on YOUTUBE

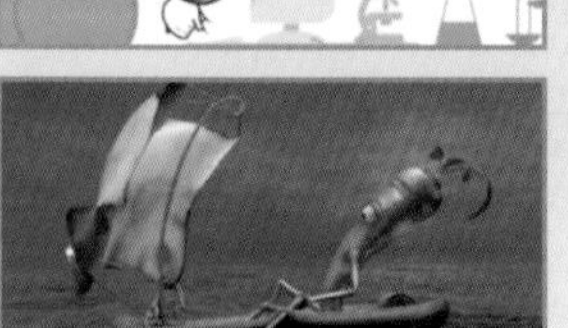

www.youtube.com/phosphorart

www.phosphorart.com

PHOSPHORART.COM

41 Pump House Close, London SE16 7HS tel:+44 (0)20 7064 4666 fax:+44 (0)20 7064 4660 email:info@phosphorart.com

YULIA BRODSKAYA

www.phosphorart.com

PHOSPHORART.COM

41 Pump House Close, London SE16 7HS tel:+44 (0)20 7064 4666 fax:+44 (0)20 7064 4660 email:info@phosphorart.com

JULIA WHATLEY

www.phosphorart.com

PHOSPHORART.COM

41 Pump House Close, London SE16 7HS tel:+44 (0)20 7064 4666 fax:+44 (0)20 7064 4660 email:info@phosphorart.com

LINDA CLARK

www.phosphorart.com

PHOSPHORART.COM

41 Pump House Close, London SE16 7HS tel:+44 (0)20 7064 4666 fax:+44 (0)20 7064 4660 email:info@phosphorart.com

DARREN WHITTINGTON

www.phosphorart.com

PHOSPHORART.COM

41 Pump House Close, London SE16 7HS tel:+44 (0)20 7064 4666 fax:+44 (0)20 7064 4660 email:info@phosphorart.com

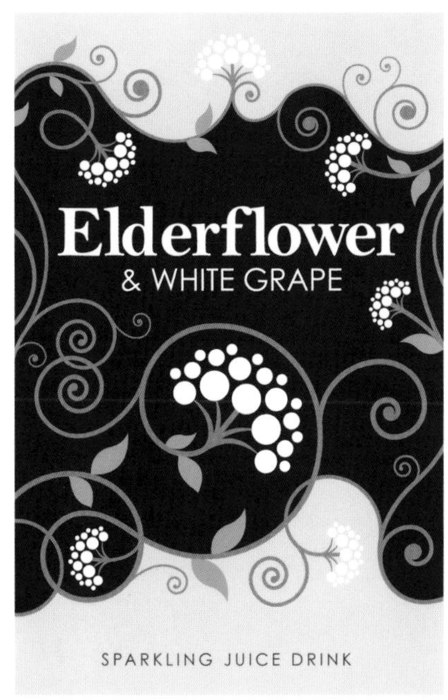

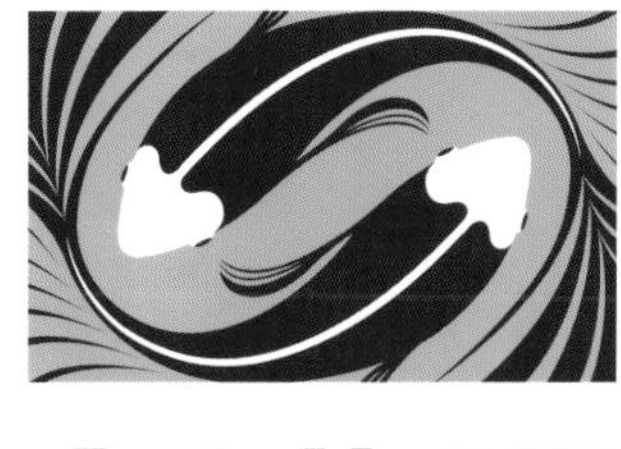

DARREN WHITTINGTON

www.phosphorart.com

PHOSPHORART.COM

41 Pump House Close, London SE16 7HS tel:+44 (0)20 7064 4666 fax:+44 (0)20 7064 4660 email:info@phosphorart.com

SILJE CAMILLA HELLESEN

PETRA STEFANKOVA

SANDRA ISAKSSON

JENNIE

PHOSPHORART.COM

41 Pump House Close, London SE16 7HS tel:+44 (0)20 7064 4666 fax:+44 (0)20 7064 4660 email:info@phosphorart.com

GEORGE MORTON-CLARK

CHRISTOPHER NIELSON

LUC JANIN

www.phosphorart.com

PHOSPHORART.COM

41 Pump House Close, London SE16 7HS tel:+44 (0)20 7064 4666 fax:+44 (0)20 7064 4660 email:info@phosphorart.com

BILL SANDERSON

BOB WILSON

PHOSPHORART.COM

41 Pump House Close, London SE16 7HS tel:+44 (0)20 7064 4666 fax:+44 (0)20 7064 4660 email:info@phosphorart.com

CHRIS STONEHILL

www.phosphorart.com

PHOSPHORART.COM

41 Pump House Close, London SE16 7HS tel:+44 (0)20 7064 4666 fax:+44 (0)20 7064 4660 email:info@phosphorart.com

JON ROGERS

www.phosphorart.com

PHOSPHORART.COM

41 Pump House Close, London SE16 7HS tel:+44 (0)20 7064 4666 fax:+44 (0)20 7064 4660 email:info@phosphorart.com

JON ROGERS

www.phosphorart.com

PHOSPHORART.COM

41 Pump House Close, London SE16 7HS tel:+44 (0)20 7064 4666 fax:+44 (0)20 7064 4660 email:info@phosphorart.com

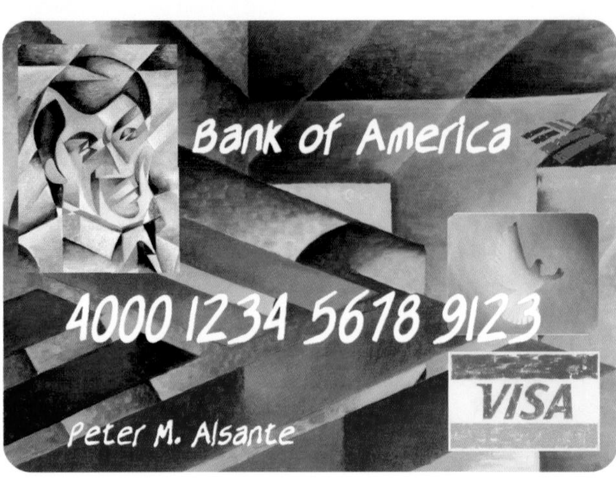

PASTICHE

www.phosphorart.com

PHOSPHORART.COM

41 Pump House Close, London SE16 7HS tel:+44 (0)20 7064 4666 fax:+44 (0)20 7064 4660 email:info@phosphorart.com

PAUL OGILSBY

www.phosphorart.com

PHOSPHORART.COM

41 Pump House Close, London SE16 7HS tel:+44 (0)20 7064 4666 fax:+44 (0)20 7064 4660 email:info@phosphorart.com

DAVE HOPKINS

PHOSPHORART.COM

41 Pump House Close, London SE16 7HS tel:+44 (0)20 7064 4666 fax:+44 (0)20 7064 4660 email:info@phosphorart.com

FIAMMETTA DOGI/AAREPS.COM

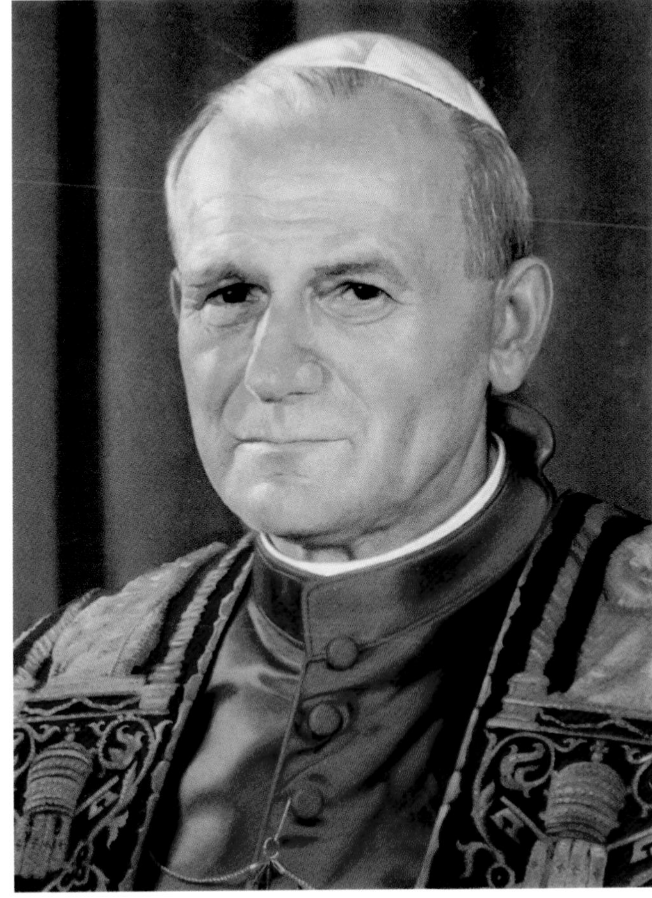

MIKE JAROSKO/AAREPS.COM

MIKE BELL

thorogood.net

contact **steve** t: +44(0) 7903 246142
contact **doreen** t: +44(0) 20 8488 3195
www.thorogood.net
draw@thorogood.net

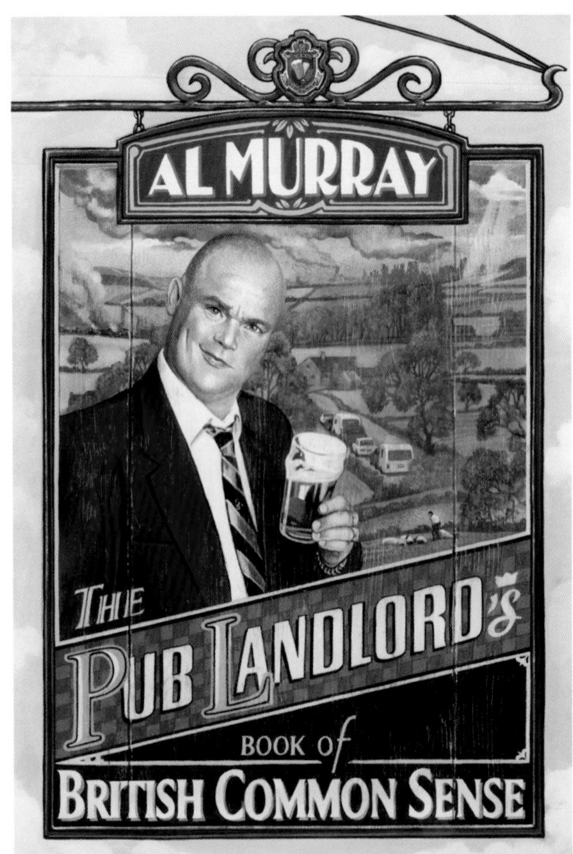

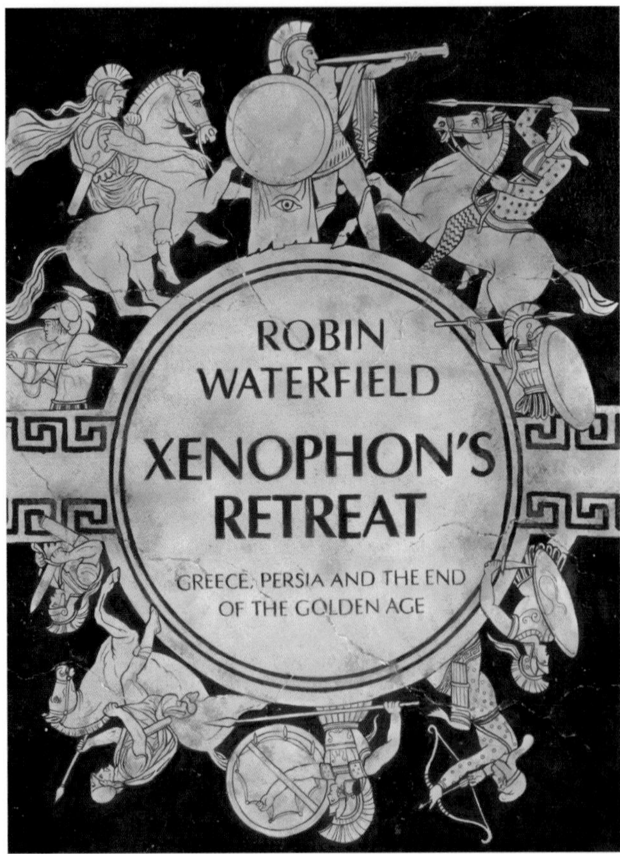

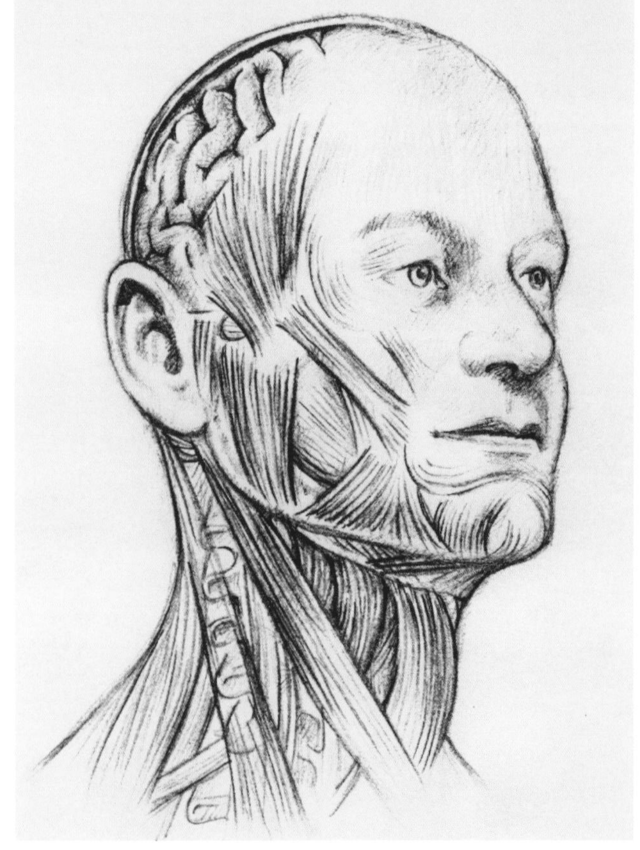

BOB VENABLES

thorogood.net

contact **steve** t: +44(0) 7903 246142
contact **doreen** t: +44(0) 20 8488 3195
www.thorogood.net
draw@thorogood.net

ROY KNIPE

KANAKO & YUZURU

www.thorogood.net

thorogood.net

contact **steve** t: +44(0) 7903 246142
contact **doreen** t: +44(0) 20 8488 3195
www.thorogood.net
draw@thorogood.net

PHIL WHEELER

ANDY POTTS

contact **steve** t: +44(0) 7903 246142
contact **doreen** t: +44(0) 20 8488 3195
www.thorogood.net
draw@thorogood.net

ANNE-YVONNE GILBERT

DAVID BROMLEY

thorogood.net

contact **steve** t: +44(0) 7903 246142
contact **doreen** t: +44(0) 20 8488 3195
www.thorogood.net
draw@thorogood.net

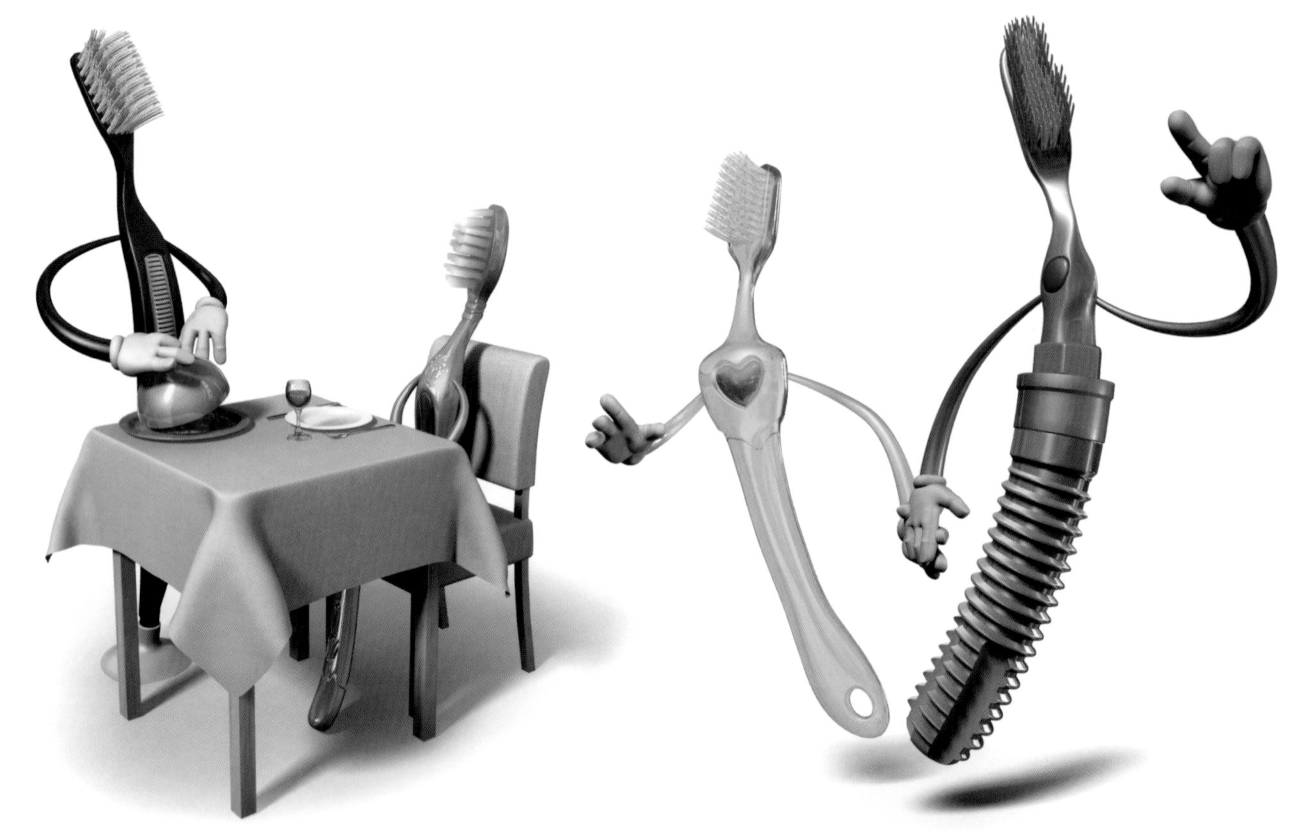

DAN HAMBE

OLIVIER LATYK

thorogood.net

contact **steve** t: +44(0) 7903 246142
contact **doreen** t: +44(0) 20 8488 3195
www.thorogood.net
draw@thorogood.net

LEO TIMMERS

PHILIP NICHOLSON

thorogood.net

contact **steve** t: +44(0) 7903 246142
contact **doreen** t: +44(0) 20 8488 3195
www.thorogood.net
draw@thorogood.net

CHRISTIANE ENGEL

NICOLA SLATER

contact **steve** t: +44(0) 7903 246142
contact **doreen** t: +44(0) 20 8488 3195
www.thorogood.net
draw@thorogood.net

SOPHIE ALLSOPP

BILL DARE

thorogood.net

contact **steve** t: +44(0) 7903 246142
contact **doreen** t: +44(0) 20 8488 3195
www.thorogood.net
draw@thorogood.net

DANIEL EGNEUS

PIOTR LESNIAK

GEOFF HARDIE

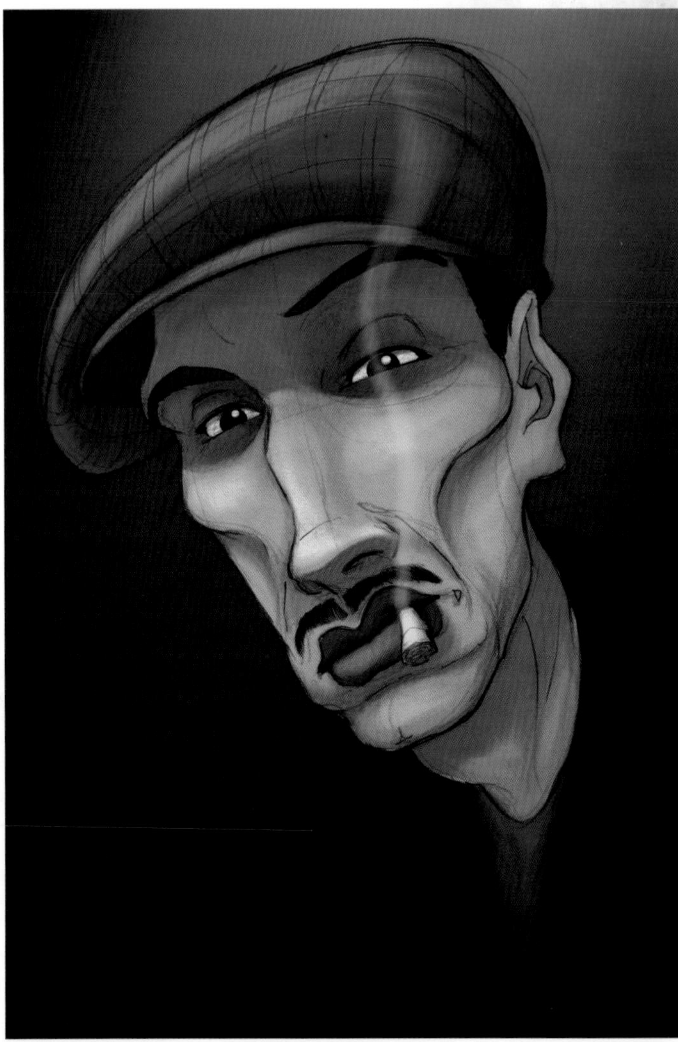

luke finlayson | advocate-art.com

a
www.advocate-art.com
mail@advocate-art.com
39 church road wimbledon village
london sw19 5dq +44 (0) 20 8879 1166
advocate art illustrate your point

paco raphael krijnen | advocate-art.com

JONNY DUDDLE

arenaworks.com

0845 050 7600 info@arenaworks.com
31 Eleanor Road London E15 4AB

JONNY DUDDLE

Central Illustration Agency
36 Wellington Street
Covent Garden
London, UK, WC2E 7BD

T: +44(0)20 7240 8925
F: +44(0)20 7836 1177
info@centralillustration.com
www.centralillustration.com

WENDY PLOVMAND

www.centralillustration.com

Central Illustration Agency
36 Wellington Street
Covent Garden
London, UK, WC2E 7BD

T: +44(0)20 7240 8925
F: +44(0)20 7836 1177
info@centralillustration.com
www.centralillustration.com

WENDY PLOVMAND

www.centralillustration.com

début **art** • Illustrators, Photographers and Fine Artists Agents
30 Tottenham Street, London, W1T 4RJ. United Kingdom
Tel: +44 (0) 20 7636 1064. Fax: +44 (0) 20 7580 7017
The Coningsby Gallery • Tel: +44 (0) 20 7636 7478
email: **info@debutart.com** • **www.debutart.com**

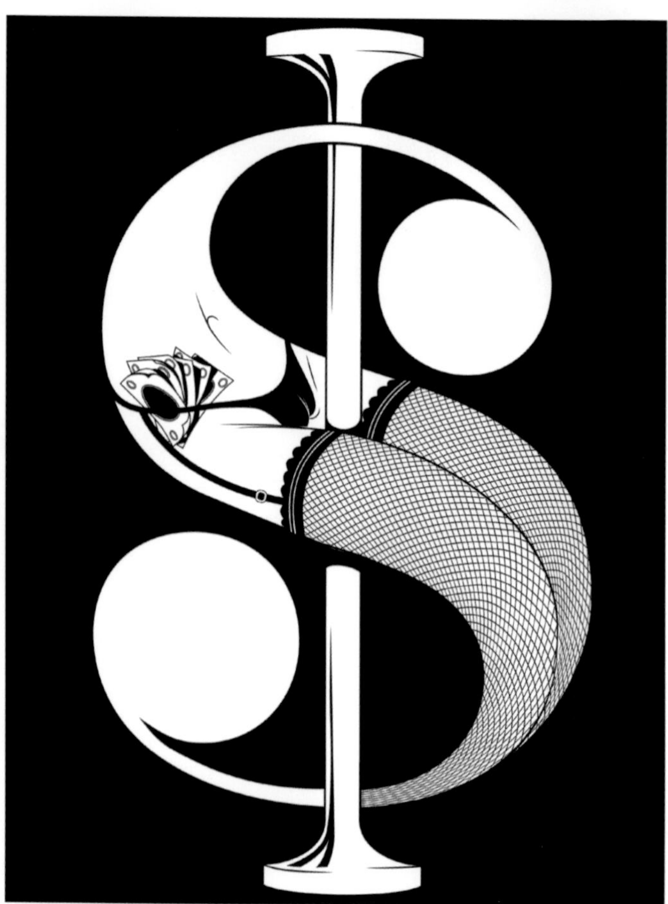

ALEX TROCHUT

www.debutart.com

début **art** • Illustrators, Photographers and Fine Artists Agents
30 Tottenham Street, London, W1T 4RJ. United Kingdom
Tel: +44 (0) 20 7636 1064. Fax: +44 (0) 20 7580 7017
The Coningsby Gallery • Tel: +44 (0) 20 7636 7478
email: **info@debutart.com** • **www.debutart.com**

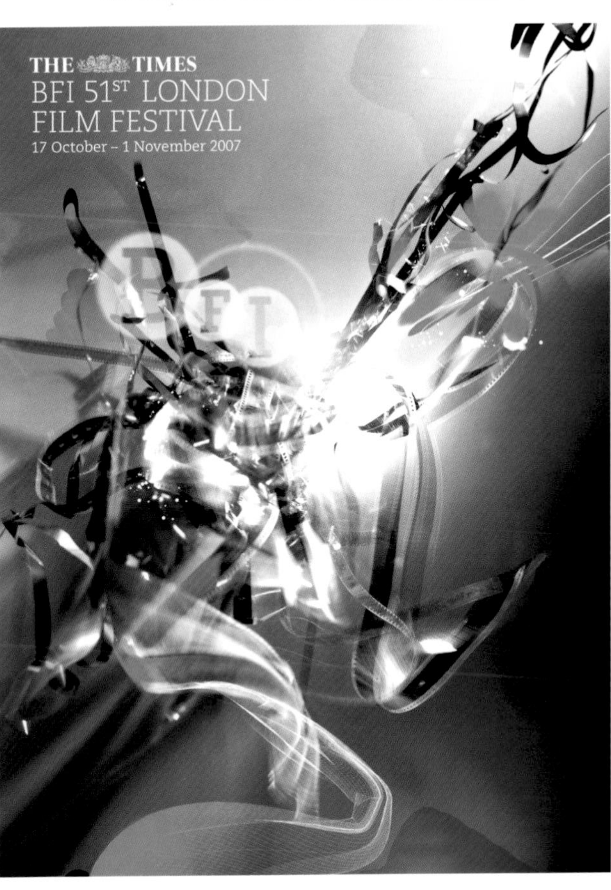

HAWAII

www.debutart.com

jelly

illustration
motion graphics
animation
creative solutions

JOHNNY MAC

www.jellylondon.com

9-10 charlotte mews, london w1t 4ef
t: 020 7323 3307 f: 020 7636 2455
www.jellylondon.com

JOHNNY MAC

www.jellylondon.com

new division

5 risborough street london se1 0hf
t:+44 (0)20 7593 0505 f:+44 (0)20 7593 0501 info@newdivision.com www.newdivision.com

BARBARA SPOETTEL

www.newdivision.com

new division

5 risborough street london se1 0hf
t:+44 (0)20 7593 0505 f:+44 (0)20 7593 0501 info@newdivision.com www.newdivision.com

BARBARA SPOETTEL

www.newdivision.com

20th edition